Invited to Faith

For no other foundation can any one lay than that which is laid, which is Jesus Christ.
—1 Corinthians 3:11

Invited to Faith
David Schroeder

The Brethren Press
Elgin, Illinois

Evangel Press
Nappanee, Indiana

Faith and Life Press
Newton, Kansas

Mennonite Publishing House
Scottdale, Pennsylvania

Scripture quotations, unless otherwise noted, are from the Revised Standard Version of the Bible, copyrighted 1946, 1952, © 1971, 1973.

A publication of The Foundation Series for Adults

Executive Director: Helmut Harder

Published by the Brethren in Christ Church, E. Morris Sider, editor; the Church of the Brethren, June A. Miller, editor; the General Conference Mennonite Church, Elizabeth Yoder, editor; and the Mennonite Church, Levi Miller, editor. Cooperative user: the Mennonite Brethren Church, Dennis Becker, editorial representative.

Designers: David Hiebert, Ken Stanley

Script for quotations: Marjorie Morse

Sketches: Pat Hykes

Credits: 83 Kathy Kline; 92, 93 Willis S. Wheatley, artist, printed with permission, Division of Mission in Canada, The United Church of Canada; 92, 93 text by Glen Horst; 99 chart by Alice Suderman; 111 Ken Stanley

Invited to Faith

Contents

5

Foreword

The invitation to faith is a continuing aspect of life. It is as old as the creation accounts of the first human beings, and as new as each individual's response to the decisions of today. God, through his active presence in the lives of people—in the past, in the present day, and in the days to come—issues the invitation, and each person must decide how to respond.

Invited to Faith invites adults to an intentional look at this ongoing agenda of life—God's action and our response to God's action. The book gives a biblical-theological outline of the foundations of the call to Christian faith. Beginning in the Old Testament, major themes of the Christian faith are traced through the Scripture and through the life of God's people. Themes of creation, the fall, promise and fulfillment, salvation and deliverance, covenant and community, the kingdom of God, and the prophetic vision, are presented. The dynamic sweep of these themes can be fully appreciated as they are followed from Old Testament beginnings, through the New Testament, and on into the life of the people of God today.

The life, death, and resurrection of Jesus is shown to be the fulfillment of these themes of faith—the key that opens the door to a fuller understanding of God's action in the world and God's call to each person for a faithful response.

The author, David Schroeder, has followed a unique approach in addressing these themes of the faith. Writing from the perspective of the active, dynamic, ongoing work of God, he uses the verb form (God is creating, judging, covenanting, reigning, etc.), rather than the more common noun form. This draws the reader into new awarenesses of God's activity in the world; it calls the reader to be a participant, not just a spectator, in God's work.

The first unit of this course, "Understanding the Christian Faith," invites the reader to an in-depth consideration of the major emphases of biblical faith. The second unit, "Faith Pilgrimage Through Life's Stages," looks at the developmental tasks of adults, emphasizing the relationship between faith in Christ and all stages of this adult pilgrimage.

In *Invited to Faith,* David Schroeder has given us a book which calls for a new look at our faith and the impact it has on our everyday lives. We will be challenged by the faith history of the past; we will be called to respond in faithfulness and obedience to God's present activity in each today; we will catch a new vision of hope for God's reign in the future.

Invited to Faith is the second in a series of eight studies in The Foundation Series for Adults. (See the inside back cover of this book for an outline of the entire curriculum.) The purpose of this curriculum is to provide learning materials for adults which reflect those distinctive aspects of the Christian faith which are emphasized in the Anabaptist vision of the people of God. This curriculum is to help examine this vision as it relates to the Bible and to our life of faithfulness in the church today.

Our hope is that these purposes may be met as these materials are used by individuals and by study groups in the congregation.—June A. Miller, editor.

Introduction

The invitation to faith focuses on God's revelation to his people. In this book we will consider the acts of God through which people have been invited to faith. Through God's revelation in history, people have come to know who God is and how they might respond to him. God's acts of creating, judging, saving, covenanting, and ruling are all a part of this on-going revelation. All these acts of revelation move toward God's supreme revelation in Jesus Christ.

Major attention will be given to the events of revelation. Through these events the people learned to know God; in the light of these events the people responded to God and gave witness to their faith. Today we have in the biblical record a witness to their faith in God.

The acts and events of revelation, the acts of God, will be the focus of this study.

We often have a tendency to turn acts and events too quickly into doctrinal statements. Doctrinal statements have their place, but they must not be placed at the beginning. They will come at the end, as the conclusion of our study. Even then they will not be simply statements *about* God, for doctrinal statements are most significant when they are an actual expression of our faith. To focus first on doctrinal statements would be putting ourselves and our faith as the focal point; we will instead allow the faith of the biblical writers to be our focus. And even as we look at their faith, we must see it as a response to the acts of God. God begins the action and the events of revelation. Through God's action we are invited to faith.

So God's revelation is our invitation to faith, and we are to respond to this invitation. The appropriate response to God the creator is worship and praise; the appropriate response to God's judgments is repentance and a return to his will; the appropriate response to salvation is thankfulness and service. As we observe God's acts in history, we will see how they were Israel's invitation to faith and discover that they are our invitation to faith as well.

God's actions are ongoing and continuing even unto the present.

God not only *was* the Creator; God *is* the Creator. In this study we will use, wherever possible, the verb form (God is creating) to give this ongoing creative action full expression. To use the noun form (God is the Creator) gives an image of God as originally creating the world, but not necessarily as actively creating in the present. This ongoing creative action of God will be emphasized in each chapter. The way in which God's presence and person was revealed in the past is also how God comes to us in the present.

Often these events have been studied through the doctrines of creation, fall, redemption, covenant, kingdom of God, eschatology, and Christology. What this does, however, is to change verbs into nouns. It changes acts of revelation and response to God's acts into doctrines about God. In our study of these events, we will emphasize what God did and does; we will look at people's response to God's acts. In this experience, we ourselves will be called to respond; we will be invited to faith.

The revelation of God builds on the people's prior understandings and experiences of God.

Once Israel understood God as the one who comes with the promise to reveal himself, they never forgot this truth. They were always looking for the promises of God and were careful to note signs of the fulfillment of God's promises. In this way, building on their experiences of God's keeping his promises, they gradually came to recognize Jesus as the promised Messiah.

10

When God revealed himself through the Exodus, Israel knew God both as one who keeps his promise and, additionally, as one who saves. They began to understand God as a saving God as well as one who keeps promises. In this way, each new revelation of God builds on earlier understandings or revelations.

We today have this history of God's revelation recorded in the Bible. Added to the biblical record is the history of God's revelation to the church through the years. Both of these records add to our understanding of God's revelation. *Each event of revelation has a continuing history.*

Each event is interpreted and reinterpreted in the history of salvation. Thus Moses speaks of an angel or messenger who will lead the people into the place God has provided (Exod. 23:20). Notice how this is then interpreted in the light of the Exile by Malachi (Mal. 3:1) and Isaiah (Isa. 40:3); it is further interpreted in the New Testament by Mark in relation to John the Baptist (Mark 1:2-3).

We must be careful to note that what is begun at one point as an initial insight into God's revelation is often completed much later. This study will try to show that all of God's revelations to Israel culminate in Jesus Christ. But we also need to be aware that Jesus himself points to the future consummation of the revelation given in him. *Each event of revelation remains open to the future, open to fulfillment.*

The interpretation of these acts of revelation are left open in the Scriptures to God's action in the future. None is closed off. God begins with a people where they are and leads them through promise and salvation to a point where they commit themselves to do his will. This openness to future growth and commitment happens again and again throughout the history of God's people.

God is not interested in achieving a static state, but wants rather a dynamic, ongoing, growing relationship with people. This includes us, personally. God always leads us on to a new and fuller understanding of his will. As we follow God's will, we are separated more and more from the ways of the world and grow into deeper relationship with God. *Each of the invitations to faith, whether through God's work of creation, salvation, or promise, encompasses the whole.*

11

The various chapters of this book are variations of the same theme. They all deal with God's revelation of himself through his mighty deeds and they all constitute for us an invitation to faith.

Our hope is that in presenting the material in this thematic way several things may happen to us.

1. We may become more conscious of God's presence in our own history and personal experience.

2. We may become aware that God extends the invitation to us in a variety of ways. If we respond to God as creator, savior, or covenant Lord, we will learn to know God also as the one who holds out the promise of a new life.

3. We may see that God's revelation is continuous and ongoing, both for the church and for us personally. We always learn to know more of God as we continue in his will.

4. We may see in the Scriptures a growing understanding of how God makes it possible for people to finally recognize Jesus as the Messiah of God.

5. We may see that the promise remains even now for us and will be consummated by God at the end of time. In this sense, our faith remains open to God's acts of judgment and of salvation yet to come.

The last four chapters of *Invited to Faith* are of a slightly different nature. They look at our pilgrimage of faith through early, middle, and later adulthood, and on into death. We will note some of the tasks to be faced in each of these periods in life. We have used three different ways of responding to these tasks: (1) by using the themes seen in God's revelation to us as a beginning; (2) by becoming aware of the biblical injunctions to mature in our judgments; (3) by taking the image of God and what that implies as a criterion of judgment; and (4) by seeing the promise of God in dying.

Our hope is that these four chapters will add to our understanding of God's invitation to faith, helping us to respond in a Christian way to the very practical issues faced in life. May the thematic studies of the first nine chapters and these studies of life-tasks become for us an invitation to faithful living.—David Schroeder

1.
God Is Creating

Seeking a Proper Perspective

As Christians we confess that God is the Creator, that God acted in the original creation and acts in the ongoing creation of the world. As we explore the full meaning of God as Creator and the unique message in the biblical creation accounts, the following perspectives will guide our thinking:

1. *The biblical creation accounts say that the worlds were created by the word of God.* "God said . . . And it was so" (Gen. 1:9). Sometimes when we speak of creation, our minds become filled with scientific notions and questions. We somehow expect the biblical creation accounts to address our questions about evolution and the origin of the world. But they make no attempt to do so. They are not scientific reports and do not pretend to tell us in detail how God created the world. Rather, the creation accounts simply, yet pointedly, affirm that God was and is a creating God, who brings into being that which was not.

2. *God in the long, long past created the world and God is also actively creating in our time.* At times we may be tempted to view creation only as an act in the past—finished, complete in itself, perfect. Such a view would see God creating the world at one time and then leaving it to run on its own.

Three Lions

14

To so view creation is to see God operating in a closed universe. This view leads to a static rather than to a dynamic view of the world. This would mean that the world was created good and could only get worse, not better; that the purpose of redemption was to lead us back to a once-perfect state; that the main focus of the Bible is on human sin and failure, rather than on a God who makes all things new.

Creation was not intended to bring about a static state of existence, however. The purpose of creation was to bring about a history of dynamic relationships to God.

3. *The creation accounts are a confession of faith.* In these accounts the author and his people are confessing their belief that God is the creator of all that the eye can see. These accounts are a confession that God is a creating God, working out his purposes in the world through his actions in history.

In the creation accounts we see a whole people confessing—both negatively and positively—their view of the world and their understanding of reality. Negatively, they reject polytheism (that there are many gods and that the earth came into being as a result of a conflict between the gods); they also reject pantheism (that everything is part of the divine being), and animism (that God is in all things). Positively, the creation accounts claim that God is Creator and Sustainer of the universe; that neither the world, nor anything in it, is to be worshiped; that the world and everything in it is totally dependent on the God who created it.

The creation accounts are a confession that God freely chooses to create and that his purposes are expressed in his work; they are a confession that history is being moved by God's action toward his own chosen goals. As creator God set, and even now sets, the limits of each living thing, including the limits of human freedom. Human beings are creatures and not gods and are responsible to the one who has given life to all living.

These accounts are a faith confession that God brings order out of chaos; that what God created and is creating is good—that it serves his purposes and objectives and serves to the well-being of all his creatures.

15

Contexts of Understanding

If we really want to hear what the biblical texts have to say about creation and about the God who is creating, we may be in for some surprises. Generally, we have taken Genesis 1 and 2 to be the biblical statement on creation; but there are also many other passages which speak of creation, and in a variety of ways. The context in which such statements on creation occur is important. Three such contexts are of special significance:

1. The Context of Worship. Most of the texts on creation are given in the context of worship and praise, not in the context of speculation about the world. In the hymn sections of the Psalms, Job, and Isaiah, we find frequent references to creation (Psa. 95:1-7; 8:3-8; 145:10; Job 26:7-14; 38:4-11).

These references to creation are not just doctrinal propositions or factual statements; nor are they simply a confession of faith. They are expressions of a people's relationship to God in the context of worship.[1] Not by accident does the creation account in Genesis 1 and 2 close with the Sabbath—a time to remember the creator (Gen. 2:1-4a).

A proper understanding of creation will take into account the context of worship. It is in the context of worship, and not in the interest of speculation about the world, that the biblical writers speak about creation.

2. The Context of Salvation. In Exodus 15:16-18, as the people pass through the sea, God speaks of creating for himself a new people. This suggests that the true meaning of creation is disclosed to the people in the Exodus. They knew themselves as having become a new people through their salvation out of Egypt; in and through this redemptive act God was revealed to them as Creator and Lord. This power of God to save led them to understand that God is Lord of all and is therefore the creator of all things.

The same understanding is seen in the New Testament. As soon as the early Christians knew Jesus to be Lord and Savior, they also understood that he was creator and sovereign Lord of all (John 1:1-3; Col. 1:15); this understanding they then expressed in their worship of God.

Thus we see that the people became aware of God's creating activity in their personal experiences with God.

And we also realize that our profoundest sense of knowing God as a creating God happens when we become new creatures in Christ and relate to him in worship and praise (2 Cor. 5:17).

3. *The Context of a Larger History (Story).* God, through the Exodus and through his covenant with Israel, created for himself a new people. This seems to say that the Exodus period was the beginning of the history leading to Christ and his church. How, then, do the creation accounts relate to this history?

The history of Israel is introduced by two other histories: (1) the very early history in Genesis 1—11 and (2) the history of the patriarchs in Genesis 12—50. These two histories help us understand the rest of the biblical message. The creation accounts, therefore, serve as an introduction to the larger story.

The Unity of Genesis 1—11

The creation accounts in Genesis 1 and 2 in no way stand alone; they are integrally related to Genesis 1—11. They serve as an introduction to the story of the patriarchs, which is in turn the introduction to the revelation of God to Israel and to the church of God. We need to see Genesis 1 and 2 in this wider context to understand their message.

It is evident that we have two accounts of creation, written from different perspectives and using different language (Gen. 1:1—2:4a and Gen. 2:4b—4:26). They are placed together in the biblical record, and we see them complementing and augmenting each other. Likewise, Genesis 4—11 is closely related to Genesis 1—3 (traditionally seen as the creation story) and cannot be ignored in a study of the creation.

If we interpret Genesis 1—3 in isolation from Genesis 4—11, this leads to a static view of creation and sin. The creation and the fall are always mentioned in doctrinal statements, but Genesis 4—11 is omitted. Yet these eleven chapters are one unit; Genesis 1—3 does not tell the whole story.

For example, the command to "be fruitful and multiply" is given both in the creation account (Gen. 1:28) and after the flood (Gen. 9:1). The fulfillment of the covenant given in

17

the creation story is seen in the listing of the generations in chapter 5. The command to Noah is fulfilled in the listing of the nations in chapter 10. A continuing history, not a static state, is implied by these examples. The first part is not complete without the second part.

Similarly, the command to subdue the earth (Gen. 1:28) and to till the garden (Gen. 2:15) is realized in the development and growth of human achievements (Gen. 4:17-26). We see these commands leading to the development of agriculture, the building of cities, to art, technology, and a culture. Ultimately, this leads to the people seeking to be like God in the tower of Babel incident (paralleling Adam and Eve's sin).

Work is part of the growth of the human race; but there is also the possibility of using work for self-exaltation. This is a continuing problem, not only in the personal realm (Adam and Eve), but also in society as a whole (Babel). To focus only on the personal is to omit part of the message. Thus, in our study, we will seek to always be aware of the unity of the first eleven chapters of Genesis.

Affirmations about Creation

Three basic affirmations will be significant to this study of creation and to our understanding of God's creating activity in the world:

1. God is reigning. The biblical accounts confess that everything depends on God the Creator. Everything in creation points beyond itself to the Creator, who alone ought to receive worship and praise (Psa. 24:1-2; 89:11f.; 95:1-5).

The Word of God is the ruling power which creates and controls the course of history (Gen. 1:9; Psa. 33:9; 148:5; Isa. 45:12). Through the active and dynamic Word, God accomplishes and carries out his purposes.

God is reigning and is actively engaged in the lives of people and in human history. Therefore, we ought to be able to look around us and see what God is creating even now.

2. God is creating. Creating consists of many different kinds of activities. The accounts focus on the variety of acts through which God created the worlds. God made, separated, named, placed, and blessed. Verbs highlight the

18

account; the sense of God actively creating is lost if the verbs are changed to nouns—if actions are transformed into doctrinal statements.

Claus Westermann, noted biblical scholar, suggests that there are two acts of separating (Gen. 1:6-8, 9-10); two acts of covering (Gen. 1:4-13, 14-19); two acts of giving life (Gen. 1:20-23, 24-28); and one of commanding (Gen. 1:17, 28-30). God's works cover the uninhabited world (Gen. 1:1-4) and the inhabited order (Gen. 1:5-7). The emphasis throughout is on what God does.[2]

God creates order out of chaos through his work of separation. Light is separated from darkness and does not allow the darkness (chaos) to rule. The waters above are separated from the waters below, making it possible for life to be placed on earth. That is, God creates the structures that make life possible. Without this kind of ordering or structuring, chaos could not be overcome nor avoided.

God's work of covering is of a different nature, but also belongs to his creative ability. Here God's action is indirect. God gives the earth the capacity to bring forth plants, thereby giving vegetation a separate existence in which plants and trees yield fruit, each according to its seed. The providence of God is first seen at work here, as he provides for the ongoing sustaining of the created order. The other act of covering is the rule that is given to the sun and the moon in the universe. It is this rule or order that we study in our scientific disciplines.

The work of giving life has special significance. The same word, "bara," is used as in Genesis 1:1 and Genesis 1:27. It indicates that with the creation of fish, birds, and land animals, a new level of life was created. The blessing of God is also introduced here (Gen. 1:22; 1:28; 2:3). The blessing is related to the power of fertility, to the command to be fruitful and multiply, which is spoken to both humans and animals.

God has given life, has created life to sustain itself on the earth. Both the direct creation of life and the creation through procreation manifest the creative and sustaining actions of God.

3. Persons represent God. People are called to represent God on earth and to continue his work. In both creation

*A primary purpose of the Church
is to help us
discover our gifts
and to hold us accountable
for them
so that we can enter into
the joy of creating.*

— Elizabeth O'Connor

accounts people are assigned the highest place of honor. They are said to be created in the image of God. In Genesis 2:4f. humans are mentioned first, and all else serves their need. In Genesis 1:1—2:4 humans are mentioned last and are seen as the pinnacle of God's creation. Both male and female are created in the image of God (Gen. 1:27).

The image of God does not consist of some attribute or characteristic of a person such as the will, the emotions, or reason; rather the image of God refers to the whole person—to what it means to be human. It refers to people being created with the ability to freely and spontaneously respond to God and to the world; it refers to historical beings shaping their own destinies through the way they relate and respond to each other, to the world, and to God. The very form of human existence is a reflection of the image of God!

It is clear in the biblical record that both male and female were created in the image of God, which says that all people are God's representatives. And all people, both men and women, share in God's reigning, for they are commanded to exercise dominion over the created order (Gen. 1:26-30). They share in God's giving of life as they are commanded, along with the animals, to be fruitful and multiply. They share in the work of tilling and keeping the garden. They are asked to name the animals, a work of classification like that which God himself exercises. In all these ways, they are like God. Humans are no less than co-creators with God!

Finally, if we want to know most fully what it is to be human, to be in the image of God, we must look to Jesus. For Jesus, both in his person and in his work, shows what God had in mind when he created people with the ability to respond to him in personal freedom.

In Jesus we see the image of God most clearly. Jesus manifested what people ought to be like as representatives of God. Paul says "He is the image of the invisible God" (Col. 1:15); the writer of Hebrews says "He reflects the glory of God and bears the very stamp of his nature" (Heb. 1:3). Jesus is in truth God's representative on earth; in Jesus, those who are his, share his work and ministry on earth (Col. 1:24f.).

21

*Creativeness in the world
is, as it were,
the eighth day of creation.*

Nicolas Berdyaev

Creation in Christ

The New Testament understands creation in the light of God's action in Christ, since he fulfills the promise made to Israel and brings in the new covenant, the new creation.

God's purposes in creation are revealed in Christ (Eph. 1:9-10), who is said to hold everything together (Col. 1:17) and to uphold all things with his power (Heb. 1:3). Not only is Christ the center of history; he is also the revelation of God's purpose that undergirds the whole of creation.

In Christ the new has already come: the new covenant, the new person in Christ, and the inauguration of his kingdom. Wherever God's action in Christ is effective for salvation, there God is creatively at work. Wherever people are true to the commission of God at creation, there God's creative action in the world continues. Wherever people are obedient to the call and commission of Christ, there the new humanity is called into being.

Creation and Consummation

The people of Israel experienced the lordship of God in their history and traced this back to creation. In the same way they looked forward to a time when God's purpose would be realized on earth. To believe in creation is to believe also in a consummation, an ending, because the purpose of history is grounded in the will of the creator. He is the first and the last (Isa. 48:12).

We need to think of creation as a beginning, with a corresponding end, which is other than the beginning. For if beginning and end are the same, then life is without purpose. Thus, we view creation as being good in the sense of its potential and possibilities, not in terms of a static state. Creation is good because the good can always be chosen, is always open to us. The present is also good, because God acts as creator even now, creating a new future. To so view the world is to be open to the future and to God's new creation.

Further Reflections

1. Take a closer look at the structure of the Genesis creation accounts. Often noting how a text is structured helps to make its message clearer.

Notice that in Genesis 1 creation is presented in terms of two sets of three days. Days 1 and 4 both speak of light; days 2 and 5 speak to the firmament above and below and are related to the creation of birds and fish; and days 3 and 6 speak of the earth as the place for land animals and humans.

Day 1
Separation of light from darkness (Gen. 1:3-5)

Day 4
Creation of the greater and lesser lights (Gen. 1:14-19)

Day 2
Separation of firmament above and below (Gen. 1:6-8)

Day 5
Creation of fish and birds (blessing) (Gen. 1:20-23)

Day 3
Separation of dry land from the seas (Gen. 1:9-13)

Day 6
Creation of animals and humans (blessing) (Gen. 1:24-25, 26-31)

Conclusion: The Sabbath (Gen. 2:1-4a)

We need to be cautious about thinking too literally of six days, for the writer is speaking here in terms of a parallelism. The six days are important, as they name the progressive creating activity of God. However, if we spend too much energy trying to determine whether each "day" is a 24-hour period or perhaps a 1000-year period (2 Pet. 3:8), we may miss the more important message of the creation accounts.

2. We have all probably attempted to harmonize the Genesis creation accounts and the present-day scientific understandings of the beginning of the world. Some problems arise from such attempts: (1) we may not recognize the nature of the creation accounts, nor their intended purpose; (2) we may focus too much on the message of science and make Scripture subservient to science; and (3) such attempts may lead us to believe that complete answers about origins could come from scientific investigation. And we must recognize that science cannot really speak about the beginning except in the form of theories—and theories themselves are expressions of belief rather than factual statements, though they may be based on evidence presently available.

It may be wiser to first seek to hear what the texts have to say before we attempt harmonizations with present-day understandings about the origin of the earth. We need to hear the message of the text as it was written, in the light of the purpose for which it was written. Then we can look more clearly at our understandings of Scripture and our understandings of the world. The creation accounts refer to God's ordering of the world, to the ongoing creative process. This invites us to use our minds in scientific observation so that we may be more aware of the work of God in the world. Thus, scientific studies do have their place, but they cannot replace the biblical text nor its message.

3. The creation accounts call us to an awareness of what it means to be human, to be made in the image of God. We see in these accounts that humans are distinct from God and from the animal world, and yet are intimately related to both. We see here both our possibilities and our limits in life.

To be human is to be a person who can answer to God

Come sing a song of gratitude
For gift of shelter, home and food,
For will to live as Jesus would –
For God and for our neighbor's good.

But God who made us
                from the clay,
Who makes us new with everyday,
'Tis God who gives and
                takes away.
Praise God, the life, the truth,
                the way.

Wilbur E. Brumbaugh

and who needs to relate wholesomely to other people. Our personhood comes about in our relating to people and to God.

As humans, we are historical beings, deliberating, making choices, acting with purpose toward chosen ends. In this way, we help to create a world, to shape the culture in which we live; as human beings we have a part in determining the kind of world in which we will be living.

As humans, we need work. People were commissioned to work at keeping the garden even before the Fall, and that commission continues. Meaningful, purposeful work is an integral part of being human.

4. We are also called to be co-creators with God. We are not in a position to create the absolutely new (bara); we *can* respond to the commission to procreate and to work (till and keep), to subdue (have dominion) and name the animals. In each of these areas, God invites us to share in the work of creating.

The entire human task, when carried out in obedience to God, is a participation in God's ongoing creating ministry. To become aware of God's purposes is to know what God will bless or judge; such awareness permits us to participate in accomplishing the purposes of God in history.

Think of what this task of being co-creators means for us! We ought to be seeing ourselves as creating and ordering life all the time; we ought to be creating structures toward life and ordering what is still chaotic in our world. And as we yield ourselves to the Lordship of Christ and do his will, we will participate in God's creative work in the world.

5. God created a world that is teeming with life; a world in which there is growth and development; a world in which people can have a personal, dynamic, and growing relationship with God and with other people. The possibility for dynamic and growing relationships was there before human sin and was not eliminated by sin. Creation is the beginning of history—a history of God relating to his creation, a history of people responding to God, to other people, and to the world about them.

God is as active as creator now as he was at the beginning. God is not only sustaining his creation; he is also actively creating new possibilities of life and growth. God is bringing order out of chaos now just as he did in the beginning. God is working out his purposes in the world and in history now as he did in the past.

God Invites Us

God created us personal beings. We have the ability to respond to the Creator in worship and in praise; we are also free to go our own way, rejecting God. God does not force our hand, but he does invite our positive response to his presence and his work. We are invited to respond to the Creator in faith, in trust, and in commitment.

---

1. B.W. Anderson, *Creation vs. Chaos* (New York: Association Press, 1967), p. 78f.
2. Claus Westermann, *The Genesis Account of Creation* (Philadelphia: Fortress Press, 1964), p. 12.

2.
Responding to God

God created people with the ability to freely and spontaneously respond to him. God gave humans the responsibility to be co-creators—to work with him in tending the garden, in naming the world, and in exercising dominion over the created order.

On the one hand, humans share with the rest of creation their creatureliness in that they, too, are made from the dust of the earth and will return to it in death. On the other hand, they were made in the image of God and represent God among and in all creation.

Human temptation arises out of this dual position. As humans, we are free moral agents. We can freely act, on the basis of our deliberations over what purposes and ends to follow. In this we are like God who freely chooses to act. Yet humans are not God; we are created beings. There are limits set to our freedom—limits set by God. Our human temptation is (1) to blame someone or something else for our failure to make correct choices, and (2) to forget that we are creatures and presume to be like God.

The Nature of Human Existence

The account of creation beginning with Genesis 2:4 seeks to give an answer to the question of why human life is as it is. The answer has to do not only with creation but also with the nature of human existence. The chapter 2 creation report does not conclude with a reference to the Sabbath as does the account in chapter 1. Rather, this account (Gen. 2:4b—4:26) includes creation, human sin, and God's acts of judgment and redemption.

Included in this section is the creation of the human family (Gen. 2:4b-7), the garden (Gen. 2:8-19), the command not to eat of the tree of the knowledge of good and evil (Gen. 2:15-17), the creation of woman (Gen. 2:18-25), the transgression of the commandment (Gen. 3), and the transgression against a brother (Gen. 4:1-16). This is one continuous story; the creation and the story that follows as the result of the covenant are firmly bound together.

The two narratives dealing with human sin are closely related. Human response was not only perverse toward God (chapter 3) but also against a brother (chapter 4). Human sin is seen both in disobedience to God and in the crime against the brother. The sin against God and the sin against the brother bring forth a similar response from God. In fact, God asks the same question in both instances: to Adam, "Where are you?" (Gen. 3:9), and to Cain, "Where is Abel your brother?" (Gen. 4:9). Each question echoes the other and points out our human responsibility to both God and to the neighbor.

The task of tilling and keeping the garden, and the task of naming the animals also ties together Genesis 2 and 4. Genesis 4 shows the broad lines of the beginnings of human civilization, as people continued the creative role assigned to them in creation. Here, reference is made to agriculture (v. 2), the building of a city (v. 17), nomadic life with cattle breeding (v. 20), the working of metals (v. 22), and the development of music (v. 21). All these are a fulfillment of the commission to cultivate and take care of the garden (Gen. 2:15). They are all a part of human work.

Only as we see chapter 4 in direct relation to chapters 2 and 3 will we see that the development of civilization is a command of God, and includes the division of work (specialization) and progress in art and technology.

So, in this account, three things besides creation are touched upon: (1) the command and the temptation to disobey the command; (2) the disobedience toward God and the sin towards the brother; and (3) God's acts of judgment and redemption.

The Temptation to Disobedience

In Genesis 2:15-17 we find the *command.* The narrative begins with God commanding the inhabitants of the garden not to eat of the tree of the knowledge of good and evil. Since the rest of the garden is at their disposal, they will suffer no want; the command does not demand any loss on their part. In fact, the command is intended to protect them from death (Gen. 2:17). There is no apparent need for a response of disobedience. They are free to choose the good.

Yet this command of God had a very specific purpose. Adam and Eve knew they were being addressed by God; they became aware of their personal relationship to God. The command underlined their exalted position before God—their being in the image of God, and able to answer to God.

The command introduced these first persons to their freedom—they were free to respond to God as they chose, either in obedience or in disobedience. They were not automatons, or puppets, but free agents, acting out of purposes freely chosen.

The command also made them aware of their responsibilities. They knew they stood in a relationship of responsibility and accountability to the one who issued the command. They were not completely free, responsible only to their own desires and wishes, as we sometimes think of freedom; rather they were free to relate to God responsibly.

The command also indicated the direction of action which would constitute an appropriate response. In this case, it set a limit for Adam and Eve as finite beings; it called on them to respect the difference between themselves and the Creator.

This helps us to understand why the tree is called the tree of the knowledge of good and evil. It is in terms of the distinction between good and evil that persons can declare their independence from God. Knowing good and evil allows people to chart their own course. It allows them to become masters and lords who set their own purposes and objectives in life, using people and things to serve their chosen goals. It allows people to do without God—to reject God.

The *temptation* is seen in Genesis 3:1-7. God's command brought with it the temptation to disobey the command. It placed before the hearers a choice; it addressed them in their freedom. They needed to deliberate about what they would do and to what end or purpose they would act.

The account indicates that Eve was tempted by the serpent, described as a creature "that the Lord God had made" (Gen. 3:1). In other words, the temptation comes to Eve out of the world in which she has been placed and in which she carries responsibility before God.

But how can we understand this temptation? Is it not arbitrary? No, it is not. Our human temptation to reject God's will comes not so much from human creatureliness (those things in which we are like the animal), as from our own exalted position of being made in the image of God.

God calls on his representatives to subdue the earth and to exercise dominion over what had been created. Out of obedience to God, people exercise a lordship over creation not unlike that exercised by God himself. Out of this authority, however, the temptation to defy God arises. People recognize their power and dominion and ability to subdue the earth and make it serve their chosen ends. From here, it is not far to making themselves supreme lords, usurping the place of God himself. Because people have been given power under God, they are tempted to be all powerful; because they are God's representatives on earth, people easily seek to be gods on earth.

We are never tempted as much by our weaknesses as by our strengths. A unique gift, capability, or ability readily leads to self-exaltation. Our temptations come out of the world in which we live. The greater our responsibility, the greater is the range of freedom, and the greater the temptation to forget our responsibility to God and exalt ourselves above all others, including God.

Our model in temptation, however, is not Adam and Eve, but Jesus. He too was tempted (Matt. 4:1-11) in the same way that we are tempted, but he did not yield to temptation (Heb. 4:14-16). God gave Jesus a task to set up his kingdom on earth, and he was tempted to achieve this by worshiping Satan (Matt. 4:8-10). But rather than exalting himself, Jesus sought obedience to God as a servant (Phil. 2:5-8); he was determined to do the will of God even if it meant being crucified (Matt. 26:39).

Jesus' obedience resulted in our salvation. Paul makes a comparison for us. "For as by one man's disobedience many were made sinners, so by one man's obedience many will be made righteous" (Rom. 5:19). This indicates that in temptation situations, we have the choice of obedience to God in Christ or of self-exaltation after the pattern of Adam and Eve.

The Transgression

Our study of the transgression will focus on three areas: the disobedience as seen in the Fall, the awareness of alienation from God, and the awareness of changed relationship.

1. The Fall. God invited Adam and Eve to enjoy the garden provided for them and to tend it (Gen. 2:4b-25). It is equally clear that they disobeyed the command of God (Gen. 3:1-7). They did not resist the temptation "to be like God" (Gen. 3:5) in the knowledge of good and evil.

The Fall occurred when Adam and Eve oriented themselves, not to God's word, but to the message received from the world about them. They oriented their lives to their own lordship and nature, rejecting God and seeking to play God with the world. However, this was not a necessary and inescapable consequence of human nature. It was the expression of human freedom, but clearly a freedom directed away from God rather than toward God. Human freedom is thus always a freedom within limits, limits which are set by God in creation and are made known in his command.

The temptation to sin arises not only in and out of human lordship over nature. Such temptation also arises out of our seeking to lord it over each other. Out of jealousy, anger, and a desire to control the situation, Cain slew his brother Abel (Gen. 4:1-16); this soon resulted in a society where vengeance was the rule (Gen. 4:23-24). The whole society became permeated by the same spirit of lordship and control; finally God's judgment of the flood was necessary (Gen. 6:5-7). This was still the human situation even after the flood, for human self-exaltation continued, as seen in the tower of Babel incident (Gen. 11:1-9).

The problem of sin disrupts not only our relationship to God; it also disrupts relationship with the sister and the brother, with the neighbor, and with the larger society. Sin leads the world back to chaos, and the work of God is again needed to re-create the world anew. Paul indicates that this is the story of humankind. All have sinned and come short of choosing what God has willed (Rom. 3:23); all share in the dynamics of choosing their own will (Isa. 53:6). Sin has thus affected human history all the way to the present.

2. The awareness of alienation from God. Adam and Eve did not fully realize their sin until after the transgression of God's command. Only then did they become aware of their alienation from God and hide themselves from him. Having sought equality with God, they now discovered that God was no longer close to them; rather, God confronted them as a stranger from whom they must hide.

Yet God did not leave Adam and Eve or Cain to themselves; he sought them out with his call, "Where are you?" and "Where is Abel your brother?" What they lost through their rebellion became clear only in the meeting with God after the rebellion; sin was discovered in God's seeking of the sinner. God goes after the ones who hide from him and calls them back to responsibility.

God's call to responsibility indicates that God takes human freedom seriously. Such a calling to responsibility is seen when we speak of God as judging sin. God's judgment is intended not as a condemnation, but as an attempt to win people back to their full responsibility before God. Judgment is to lead to awareness of sin and to repentance.

3. Awareness of changed relationships. Persons are not only alienated from God, but also stand exposed before others. The text indicates that Adam and Eve knew themselves to be naked and ashamed (Gen. 3:7). A play on words is used here: At first they were not ashamed (Gen. 2:25) but now in seeking to be wise ('arum, 3:6), they discover they are naked ('erom, 3:7). This means that they are ashamed in each other's presence. Their shame results from the unmasking, from being exposed for what they are. Shame indicates that a person has lost something, or that something is not right. Adam and Eve knew that it was not right to continue in this state, so they clothed themselves with what was available to them. Cain, too, became aware that his sin against God made him a fugitive and a wanderer upon the earth (Gen. 4:14). In such sin, all relationships are changed.

The Punishment

According to Genesis 2:17 and 3:3 we might expect the death sentence to be pronounced, but such is not the case. The feeble excuses—blaming the woman and the serpent—are quickly brushed aside; Adam and Eve are held morally accountable for their action. The immediate verdict of punishment, the curse, focuses on the serpent (Gen. 3:14) and on the ground (Gen. 3:17). Adam and Eve are granted grace to live, but they must live in a changed environment; in this environment neither the ground nor the animals will be their friend.

Sin, first of all, results in a changed relationship to God and to people. It also results in a changed environment. Structures and orders which have been created to undergird life are no longer functional; barriers and obstacles to earning a living and to living in peace and harmony are erected. The relationships to nature (thorns and thistles) and to one another (childbearing and subjugation) change as a consequence of human sin.

Since people are free to make choices, the choice to obey or to disobey God's command makes a real difference in the world. Such choices become a part of human history. God honors people's choices and allows them to create and fashion the kind of world for themselves that they choose. And then people have to live in the culture and the world they have created; they have to live with the consequences of their choices and actions. The consequence of choosing evil is that the relationships, structures, and orders which regulate life become inoperative or oppressive. The whole human environment changes as a consequence of sin.

In this context of sin, Adam and Eve are reminded that

human life does not last forever—"you are dust, and to dust you shall return" (Gen. 3:19). Because of their sin, life will no longer be without the fear of death.

Not only do relationships and the environment change, but woman and man experience a change in their own bodies. What was originally a blessing in their lives is now changed. Because of human sin, the woman's role becomes one of dependence and submission, and she will experience pain in childbirth. Because of human sin, man's role becomes one of dominance, and his tilling and keeping of the ground becomes a struggle with weeds and thistles. This was not the command or intent of God, but rather describes how life is as a result of human sin.

Thus childbearing and work were no longer unmixed blessings. The relationship of the man and the woman was no longer a mutual relationship as God had intended, but one of subordination and domination. All of this will need to be corrected again in the salvation to come in Christ.

How often sin turns what is intended as a blessing into a strange mixture of good and evil. Two further examples illustrate: (1) God intended for human sexuality to be a blessing to husband and wife; but how often has it been turned into a curse because of human sin? (2) God has given to us many varied gifts, full of possibility for good; yet when we use our gifts in selfish or evil ways, they become a curse for all humankind.

God's Mercy

God's mercy is available for people who sin. Even the sin of murder (Gen. 4:1-16) did not lead to capital punishment but to God's protection. This is typical of God's response to those who sin. God comes to people in mercy and grace and creates for them a new opportunity for life. Even God's judgments are not punitive, but call people back to responsibility and accountability and to repentance.

Many interpreters have seen in Genesis 3:15 a reference to Christ's victory over Satan; sometimes this has been seen as the first reference to the salvation that would come in Christ. As an understanding based on New Testament writings, this may be fitting, but it goes beyond what the Genesis text itself says. This text sees the serpent as one of God's creatures. The statement in verse 15 is part of a curse and not a promise of salvation. However, the saving grace of God is revealed in this passage. But it is seen, not in the curse spoken to the serpent, but rather in the staying of the execution of the guilty.

God's mercy and redemption is shown in many ways. God covers the nakedness of Adam and Eve when they had already tried to do so (Gen. 3:7; 3:21). God takes them from the garden so they won't eat of the tree of life and commit a greater sin. God in his mercy also provides for Cain. He declares that vengeance belongs to God and not to the people and thus protects Cain from death (Gen. 4:15). Even in the judgment of the flood, God spares the lives of Noah and his people (Gen. 6:7-8, 17-18), so that life on earth may continue. Further evidence of God's mercy and redemption is seen in the genealogies and the listing of nations (Gen. 5 and 10), which fulfill the earlier command to multiply. Even the confusion of speech at Babel is an act of God's mercy and salvation from greater sin.

God's mercy is present wherever human sin leads toward chaos and death. God acts to overcome sin and to re-create structures which will turn people to God again and to obedience to his will.

Further Reflections

1. To some extent, all humans are "in bondage to sin." We cannot avoid temptation; we have the freedom to choose for the good or for evil. We are so placed between God and the world that our ability to control and to order things leads us all too easily to feel that we are masters of our own destiny. Human greatness is our problem.

There is no denying human freedom and human power. People can do awesome things. We have technology to remove mountains and change rivers. We are tempted to think there is nothing we cannot do, given time.

2. The command of God sets limits. Human life has its divinely set limits. The command "thou shalt not . . . " comes to all of us. And often we do no better in recognizing this command than did Adam and Eve.

The range of areas in which we do not know whether we

For I do not do
  the good I want,
but the evil I do not want
  is what I do.

Now if I do what
  I do not want,
it is no longer I that
  do it,
but sin which dwells
  within me.

  —Romans 7:19-20

are transgressing human limits is growing. Is it appropriate for us to decide when death occurs (so we can transfer organs), or when to bring people back to life (resuscitation)? Is it appropriate for us to seek to control our genetic makeup? If so, who will decide what people are to be like? Is it appropriate to control people's minds with drugs or to change their basic nature? Is it appropriate to deplete the earth of its resources so that we can live but others must die? Are we, in these areas and others, in danger of over-stepping proper human limits?

3. Our response is often in terms of not fully honoring the command. Simply hearing an absolute command (thou shalt not steal—Exod. 20:15) does not solve our problem; we need to know what constitutes stealing. Trying to sort this out (for instance, is charging a 300% markup on a product stealing?), we get lost in so many relativities that we lose sight of the basic command. And yet we must honor both God's commands and the many factors in our lives that bear on the command. God's commands do speak to very concrete situations in life. They cannot remain without application.

4. We carry responsibility for the shape of the world in which we live. We use God's gifts to shape for ourselves a world of our own choosing. Our self-seeking ways affect very deeply our relationship to God and to other people. Often they create a world without God. Look at the impact our standard of living has on the rest of the world. Note how the mistreatment of a child may live on for generations; consider how our actions are never without consequences for good or evil. So we do have freedom—but with great responsibility!

When we become self-seeking, the image of God is no longer seen in our actions, for then we represent ourselves, not God. Sometimes we appeal to pseudo-gods (nationalism, individualism, or ideologies), so our self-seeking will not be exposed for what it is.

Yet when we respond to the will of God in trust and obedience, we again represent God on earth; at such times, that which is of God can be seen in our lives.

5. Sin is personal transgression. It is a transgression for which we are personally accountable. However, the

effects of sin extend much further than our personal selves. The effects of sin work themselves out in the world from generation to generation. We alone do not suffer the consequences of our sin; others are equally affected. Sin changes the world.

So, sin is not only personal transgression; sin is also deeply embodied in the fabric of society and in the structures of society. Both personally and as a society, we need to be called to repentance and to new commitment to God's will.

God Invites Us

The judgment of God on our sins is an invitation to confess our sins before God and seek his forgiveness through Jesus Christ, our Lord and Savior. In God's judgment, we are invited to turn around, to return to the Creator, to seek his face. We are invited to stand firm in God's strength, not yielding to the temptation to seek our own ends but rather doing the will of God. Judgment calls for repentance and rededication to God.

3.
God Promises

Everyone who has attended Sunday School is familiar with God's promise to Abraham. It has been told over and over again. But have we missed something of the theological significance of that event? This promise to Abraham is not just an isolated event. Throughout the Bible, God is seen as one who promises and fulfills. This concept of promise and fulfillment is a way of seeing God at work in history, in the life of a people, in the lives of all persons. It describes the way in which God comes to people and reveals himself to them. It invites people to faith, to commitment, and to obedience; it invites people to experience the fulfillment of God's promise in their lives. In this sense the biblical concept of promise and fulfillment is as significant for us as it was for Abraham and Sarah.

The Nature of Promise

The nature of the promise of God can perhaps be best understood if we first look at the nature of our relating with other people. Promise and fulfillment are also themes in our relationships to other people. When two people meet who have never met before, they may already read a promise in each other's eyes or actions. They perceive that the other promises to be a friend. If they commit themselves to that promise, their history together may show signs of fulfillment; if so, they will say that they are indeed friends. If, however, their experiences do not show signs of fulfilling the promise of friendship, then they cannot affirm a friendship. Thus the process of revelation is one of promise, of acting on the promise, and of becoming aware of the signs of fulfillment of the promise. If there are no signs of fulfillment, the promise itself remains open to question.

We come to know God in like manner. God reveals himself to us in the form of a promise. It is always a promise that is related directly to the crises in our lives, to our needs, and to our history. The promise comes to us as a real possibility, as an invitation to faith. If we respond to that promise in faith and trust, commit ourselves to it, and act upon it, then it has the possibility of producing signs of fulfillment that will act as an assurance that the promise is indeed of God.

Notice that the revelation in the form of a promise does not become knowledge nor become a part of our lives until we respond to it in faith and trust. Fulfillment cannot come without our obedient response to the promise. We can only know the truth of God's promise, of God's revelation, as we respond to it. This is different from the kind of knowledge we receive about things where we can look and see and establish actual fact. Knowledge of God is personal knowledge. It comes about through dialogue, through revelation and response; knowledge of God is not completed until the revelation, in the form of a promise, has been responded to and has been confirmed in history.

Discerning the promises of God

We have often referred to the promises of God to his people. We have noticed the promises of God to Abraham, to Moses, to David, and to us through Jesus; we have encouraged people to take the promises of God seriously. Yet, we need to go further in our understanding of the promises of God. We must relate the promises appropriately to our own lives. We need to discern the promises of God to us in our time, in our concrete history, in our day-by-day decisions related to work, to relationships with others, and to the world at large. The promises of God need to take on flesh in our history.

41

The promise-fulfillment way of thinking about our relationship to God reminds us that we are responsible for discerning the will of God for our time. Such discernment takes into account both the Scriptures and the situation in which we live. We must seek a further and deeper understanding of the Word of God—what its message was in its own time, how that message applied to life then, and what it says to our own time. We must also seek deeper understandings of the context in which we live our lives— understandings of our culture, of the immediate situation and our weaknesses, of the principalities and powers that operate in our time, and the pressures that cause us to lean in one direction or another. All of these need to be considered when we seek to discern God's promises for us.

In discerning God's will for our day, we must study both the Word and the world. For the Word has to apply to specific situations in our day. And we find ourselves in some situations that were not known in biblical times. We deal with the hunger and poverty produced by our economic systems; we are confronted with employment and job changes; we deal with abortion and other medical questions introduced by modern technology; we are concerned with nuclear problems and the use of power; daily, we face issues that were not known in biblical times. And in all of these situations we need to discern what the promise of God is to us.

We also need to look at the promises of God in community terms, discovering God's promise in relationship to the whole community. The promise relates not only to individual decision-making, where each person makes up his own mind; the promise relates also to the discernment and decision-making of the community. We need to be a seeking community of believers, which together studies the Word of God; together we need to interpret the society in which we live and decide the extent to which we cooperate with the movements of our day or go counter to them. In all of this, the discernment of the faith community is needed.

The Promise of God

Genesis 1—11 has served as the introduction to the larger story; it has provided the framework within which the rest of the story will be understood. This introduction has shown God to be Creator and Lord, creating the possibility of life and sustaining it. It has shown that creation is good, but is constantly affected by sin and human freedom as people seek to be co-creators with God. It has also shown the continuing effect of human sin in history and God's acts of setting limits to evil and granting grace to the sinner.

Beginning with Genesis 12, the focus is on God's choosing for himself a people through the call of Abraham. God calls to himself a people who will respond to him in faith and obedience as he leads them to become a people through whom all the nations of the earth will be blessed.

In one sense, Genesis 12—50 is also an introduction. It is introductory to God's establishing of a covenant with Israel. It provides the background for understanding the Exodus, the giving of the law, and the establishing of Israel as the people of God through whom the nations would be blessed. This introduction clarifies how God works in the world. By choosing one (Abraham), God chooses a people (Israel), and out of that people come those who will be ministers to many.

This second introduction focuses on the promises of God to Abraham, Isaac, and Jacob; and on Abraham's obedience to the promise. Here the theology of promise and fulfillment, which continues throughout the history of God's people, has its historical roots. If we understand the nature of these promises and what they say about God's working in history, we will also understand how God works in our time. We will know how God comes to us with his promises and how we are to respond to them.

So, we see Genesis 12—50 focusing on the promises of God. In fact, this section begins and ends with references to the promise of God. Coming at the beginning of a larger history (starting with the Exodus), Genesis 12—50 informs us that the promises of God will be an important theme in the subsequent history.

Several general observations about God's promises to the patriarchs will be helpful. While the promise to Abraham is a familiar story, we can always find new perspectives from which to view the account. Consider the following:

1. Abraham had already left Ur of the Chaldeans. Terah, his father, had already brought Abraham and Sarai and Lot to Haran and settled there (Gen. 11:31).

2. God spoke to Abraham in this new land, away from the land of his ancestry and the land of his birth.

3. Being uprooted, Abraham would have been concerned about his future: How would he feed his family? How would he sustain his family, as he had no son?

4. God's promises related directly to the life concerns that Abraham was experiencing. God came to him in grace, responding in a saving way to his need for a son and a land.

We notice here a characteristic of God's coming to his people at all times. God's coming is accommodated to people's needs, to those things that bind or enslave a people.

Five specific promises are significant in God's promise to Abraham:

1. There is the promise of "blessing" (Gen. 12:1-3). All the other promises seem to flow from this general blessing, adding detail and further interpreting its meaning. The blessing for Abraham includes many descendants and future greatness. Of even more significance, all the nations will be blessed through Abraham (Gen. 18:19; 21:1; 22:15-18; 26:1-5). Here is the beginning of a key theme in the biblical story—that God is always interested in blessing the whole human family.

2. The promise of land is given (Gen. 12:7). As Abraham goes forth to the land of Canaan, God promises to him the very land he is walking on. This is the promise of both a new home and new pasture for his cattle. This means escape from the threat of starvation and freedom from the enemy. This promise is restated many times (Gen. 13:14-17; 15:7-21; 17:8).

3. The promise of a son and posterity. This promise is already hinted at in the promise of blessing. It is made more specific in the promise of a son (Gen. 15:1-6; 16:11; 17:15-21; 18:10-14) and of descendants (Gen. 15:5; 16:10).

4. The promise of God's presence. This promise is made to Isaac (Gen. 26:3, 24) and to Jacob, and is a dominant theme of Genesis 26—50. God promises to be with the patriarchs in their wanderings; this promise of God's presence is a part of the command to remain (Gen. 26:1-3),

I am God Almighty ....
I will make my covenant
   between me and you...
I will make you the father
   of a multitude of nations...
I will give to you
   the land of your sojournings...
And I will be your God.

paraphrased, Genesis 17: 1-8

to move (Gen. 46:1-3) or to return (Gen. 31:3).

5. The promise of covenant. This promise is given in the words "I will be your God" (Gen. 17:7-8); it is later spelled out in detail in the covenant at Sinai (Exod. 29:45). This promise is a link between the patriarchs and the nation of Israel. This promise of covenant provides the basis of an abiding relationship.

The Nature of the Promises to Israel

The promises in the Old Testament are part of a whole complex of oracles of God. They are depicted as having been directly given by God to the patriarchs. Seemingly, they were not mediated in any way, but were a direct revelation from God.

Another aspect of many of these promises is that they are unconditional. What God promises is what will be (Gen. 22:15-18). Fulfillment ultimately does not depend on any condition outside of God's own resolve. This gave assurance to Israel when they feared their own survival.

Later, the promises are linked to the call of Moses to lead the people to the promised land. The promises guided the people in their journey and were the source of their strength as well as the object of their rebellion. God's promise gave continuity to Israel's history.

In like manner the promises to David were in recognition of the promises to Israel (2 Sam. 7:28-29), and looked to ultimate fulfillment in the coming of the Messiah. Each new pledge was oriented towards the initial promise to the patriarchs and toward all the generations to come (1 Kings 8:15-25).

Confidence in the promise was the essence of hope (Psa. 18:30; 119:116); discontent with the fulfillment of the promise was the root of sin (Psa. 106:24). And the prophets declared boldly that the promise had implications for the actions of national leaders.

Most of all, the early church saw in Jesus Christ the fulfillment of the promises to Abraham and to Israel. Paul sees the promise to Abraham including all people, for God included in that blessing all of Abraham's descendants and heirs, whether Jew or Gentile. In a similar way, Jesus Christ is Abraham's seed (Gal. 3:16) and in him are incorporated all of Abraham's offspring (Gal. 3:29). Thus all who live by faith in the promise are children to whom the promise is given.

From Promise to Fulfillment

We will understand better many things about God's word and work as we see more clearly how God comes to us through promise and fulfillment.

1. The promise comes to people in a moment of revelation. A moment of revelation is one in which God is present to us, and through his Spirit communicates a promise to us. The promise is directly related to our situation, to the things we are struggling with or deliberating about. It deals with those things that are in flux.

2. The promise carries with it its own convicting power. Somehow we are assured that if we act in harmony with God's promise, our actions will be blessed of God and will lead to life and health—to salvation.

3. The promise is convincing and it calls for a response. It calls for a response of faith, acceptance, and obedience. The truth of the promise cannot be known apart from commitment to the promise.

Sometimes it is hard to fully appreciate this fact. We want to know before we commit ourselves; we want cash in hand first. But in personal relationships, it does not work that way. You cannot know whether a person is honest until you have placed trust in him or her; you cannot say someone is your friend until you have responded to each other as friend to friend; you cannot know that someone loves you until that person becomes vulnerable to you.

Any promise, whether from God or from other persons, invites our response; it asks for commitment on the basis of faith and trust.

4. The confirmation of the truth of the promise comes in and through obedience. As Abraham and Sarah obeyed God's promise, God gave to them the signs of fulfillment. First there was a son, then the increase of family and herds, and finally the cave of Machpelah where Sarah was buried. Each of these was a sign that God was honoring the promise made earlier. And so, Abraham died in faith, knowing that the promise that had been made earlier would be

fulfilled to the succeeding generations (Heb. 11:8-12).

5. There were, however, not only true promises but also false ones. Often when promises were made by prophets who spoke for God, false prophets contradicted the messages. It was difficult to know who spoke for God when both prophets claimed to do so, and yet gave opposite counsel. Whenever this happened the people said in effect "We will wait and see whom God honors"—we will see which prophet's word will be fulfilled. Once the true prophet's word found confirmation in the fulfillment of the word, the people knew which promise was of God.

6. Once the promise is fulfilled and confirmed of God, it becomes the basis for the proclamation of the sure word of God. It now carries the same level of assurance that we have when we know and trust a person fully—we would stake our lives on that person's integrity. The strength of the message lies in the fact that it was confirmed, not by our own doing, but by God in the ongoing history of the people.

Further Reflections

1. God comes to us with his promise, not in a pre-packaged set of knowledge or a set of doctrines. God comes to us with a call to commit ourselves without reservation to his promise. Even God's commands are given in the context of promise. To Abraham it was "Go . . . and I will . . . " To the disciples Jesus said, "Follow me and I will make you fishers of men." Even the law was given with the promise of life.

God's promise to us is a recognition of our freedom to respond; it is an invitation to do his will. Thus it is always related directly to the things we are deliberating about, to the things we must do.

In every decision about what to do, we try to discern that action which holds out the promise of blessing. When we devote ourselves to study, we do so because it promises to be useful to us in life. When we go on vacation, we promise ourselves rest and relaxation. With the birth of a child comes the promise of a whole life-time.

2. We need to be more aware of God's promises in our every day work. To receive such promises, we have to be

sensitive to God's leading in our lives. God's promises may come to us in dreams and visions that suddenly show signs of fulfillment. They may come to us through friends and loved ones who make suggestions about what we ought to do. They may come through circumstances that call forth possibilities not seen before. God's promises may concern relationships, decisions we need to make, or possibilities for active involvement in our world.

3. The Word of God comes to us with promise. And yet the writings of Scripture must always be interpreted. For instance, Israel was told not to work on the Sabbath, but exactly what constituted "work" had to be interpreted. We are not to steal, but the exact meaning of stealing varies a great deal among people who are seeking to be true to this command. Thus, we must always interpret the meaning of Scripture for our lives.

Every such interpretation, however, comes to us as a promise. It promises to be God's word to us, but we will not know that fully until we have responded to it in obedience.

4. The Church needs to be a discerning community. In the fellowship of believers we need to receive the promises of God regarding many issues people face today. When the church seeks to find the will of God with respect to war taxes, abortion, divorce, and many other issues, it is seeking the way which promises to be of God.

To so discern the promises of God and to live in accordance with them as a community of faith models a new way of living; truly this shows forth a new community in which God is at work.

5. It is good to be constantly deliberating about what to do with respect to various issues in the church. Such deliberation indicates that we are looking for the promise of God in all areas of life and are inviting the Spirit of God to lead us to the truth.

God Invites Us

Through his promises God invites us to respond to him in faith and trust. We are invited both to commit ourselves to the promise and to experience the fulfillment of the promise in our lives. We are invited to obedience—an obedience through which we come to know God more fully.

4.
God Is Saving

Salvation is what it is all about. The whole Old and New Testament focuses on the saving acts of God. This saving activity of God is much broader than simply individual salvation. Rather, God's salvation is *personal* salvation, which includes the individual, all the many human inter-relationships, and the material culture and world as well.

We have already noted the saving interest and acts of God in Genesis 1—11. God did not seek to destroy, but chose to redeem the sinful. Even God's acts of judgment, such as the expulsion from the garden and the dispersal at Babel, were acts of judgment intended to bring people back to a saving relationship with God.

The history of the patriarchs also focuses on God's saving intentions by calling attention to God's promises of posterity, of land and food for people and beasts. Through his promise God calls attention to his saving purposes with humankind. God's purpose is to bless not only Abraham but also all the nations of the earth.

But Israel experienced God as a saving God most fully in the Exodus event. The people were slaves in Egypt, powerless to free themselves, their lives in danger. But God came to them; and in a miraculous way they were set free to serve the living God. This experience of salvation was never to be forgotten. It became Israel's living example of God's saving will and work. And this Exodus event gives us a basic understanding of the saving work of God.

50

Salvation through Liberation

God had acted to prepare his people for the moment of liberation. Their lot was heavy, and was getting worse with every attempt to improve things for themselves (Exod. 5). But God had already saved and equipped his servant Moses for the work of setting the people free. God's action saved Moses from the death of drowning; in the courts of Pharaoh and in the flight into the desert, Moses was prepared for his later work. In the desert, God called Moses and introduced himself as the God of the patriarchs (Exod. 3:13-15); here, God commissioned Moses to go to his people Israel and bring them out of the land of Egypt (Exod. 3:16-17). God told Moses that Pharaoh would offer resistance, would need to be convinced through signs and wonders to let the people go, but would not be able to hold the people in bondage.

Exodus 14 describes the crossing of the Red Sea. Pharaoh, thinking that the people could now be easily overcome, gave pursuit. Even some of the people of Israel feared that all was lost, wailing that it would have been better to stay in Egypt as slaves than to die in the wilderness (Exod. 14:10-12). But Moses, assured of God's presence with them, said "Fear not, stand firm, and see the salvation of the Lord, which he will work for you today; for the Egyptians whom you see today, you will never see again. The Lord will fight for you, and you have only to be still" (Exod. 14:13-14). Then God gave the command to go forward. The east wind blew back the waters; the people crossed over the sea, with the cloud shielding them from the Egyptians (Exod. 14:19-20) and the pillar of fire leading them during the night (Exod. 13:21-22).

Exodus 15 is a celebration of this saving event. This song of Miriam looks back in jubilation at the Exodus from Egypt as the crowning act of God's salvation. Poetic form and poetic imagery portrays this historic event and makes it also an act of commemoration and worship. This song speaks of God as having gained a victory over Pharaoh's armies. In this sense God is a man of war, for he has overcome those who live by power and might. The emphasis, however, is on the salvation God has brought to his people. "Thou hast led in thy steadfast love the people whom thou has redeemed, thou hast guided them by thy strength to thy holy abode . . . The Lord will reign forever and ever'' (Exod. 15:13, 18).

The History of Salvation

We have seen that people's choices, whether for good or for evil, make a difference in the world. Such choices become a part of history and of culture. In the same way, God's saving acts can be traced through the history of his people. Salvation is as real and as concrete as the sin and bondage which it overcomes. Thus if humankind is to be saved, God must work in history; God must turn people and their history from the sinful process of death and destruction to a process that furthers life, wholeness, and peace.

As we have already seen, God, through his promise, awakened in Abraham and his people an awareness of his presence and an openness to trust him; the people were committed in faith to obey God's call. This was already a promise of salvation; God had given the people provisions for life, for descendants, and for being a channel of blessing to the nations. But the saving purpose of God became even more apparent and visible in the Exodus. Literally, Israel was to stand still and see the salvation of God. In and through their liberation from bondage, Israel understood that it was God's hand acting in their history; that God's actions were an expression of his will to save and to set free his people. Israel no longer needed to question or debate the nature and purposes of God, for God had revealed his saving intentions in ways that all people could see.

This saving event of the Exodus not only illustrated what God had done; it also was seen as a symbol of how God acts in all settings to free his people. From this action of God, Israel knew that God was the Lord of history and Creator of all. From this saving event Israel also came to know that all of history would move to the realization of the Kingdom of God. As they knew God to be Lord, they also knew that his will would ultimately triumph on earth. Through the Exodus event Israel knew that whatever the events of history, God would be present as the one who saves and sends messengers of salvation.

In the history of Israel following the Exodus, this saving

Three Lions

53

event helped them determine what was of God and what was not of God. Any person, king, or foreigner, who acted in a saving way towards God's people was recognized as a servant and messenger of God, sent by God to accomplish his saving will.

Even the prophets evaluated the rule of the kings according to this Exodus event, determining whether a king was serving God or simply doing what was right in his own eyes. The prophets knew that the salvation of God, begun at the Exodus, would be finally accomplished in God's judgment and salvation at the end of history.

Moving out of the saving event of the Exodus, the prophets also told of a servant-saviour who would inaugurate a new kingdom of peace and wellbeing. They saw the time when the Messiah, the anointed of God, would come and free the people from sin, claiming them as his servants. On the basis of the Exodus, they foresaw the salvation of God coming in Jesus Christ; they knew that God had revealed himself not only as a mighty Lord over all things, but also as a saving God.

In the Exodus, God became known to the people as a saving God. They had seen it with their eyes; they had experienced the salvation of God in their lives. They now knew who God was; they knew how God stood toward his creation and people. They no longer needed to fear, for they knew God intended their salvation.

Salvation through Sacrifice

Sin was a reality that needed to be addressed, even after God had made a covenant with Israel and had given the law as an indication of his will for Israel. But the people often transgressed the law and disobeyed the commands of God. So sin continued as a reality in spite of Israel's knowledge of the law. God again showed mercy and provided a covering for sin. Leviticus 4 tells the story.

If someone sins unwittingly, a young bull must be provided for an offering. The sinner must lay hands on the bull and have it slain by the priest. The priest then sprinkles the blood before the Lord seven times, putting some on the horns of the altar and pouring the rest at the base of the altar. In this instance the sinner identifies with the sacrifice in the laying on of hands. The bull is then offered as a sweet-smelling sacrifice to God. In effect the sinner is saying "As I sacrifice this animal, so I give myself to God." The sacrifice did not magically atone for sin; rather, God recognized the sacrifice as covering the sin.

This sacrifice is not to be confused with the scapegoat where the *sin* is transferred in the laying on of hands (Lev. 16:20-22). In this case the goat is driven into the wilderness and not sacrificed.

The practice of offering a sacrifice for sin became a symbol for salvation. It presented a vivid portrayal of the worshipers' commitment to God, and God's acceptance of the sacrifice as a covering for sin.

The New Testament builds on this understanding of salvation through sacrifice: Jesus offered himself as a sacrifice once and for all (Heb. 9:28); those who identify with Christ in his death will be raised to newness of life (Col. 2:12). From this understanding of salvation, Paul admonishes us to "present your bodies as a living sacrifice, holy and acceptable to God, which is your spiritual worship" (Rom. 12:1).

Salvation in Christ

The salvation which began in the Exodus looked forward to a messenger of God, an anointed servant who would come to bring in God's righteous rule among the people. During Jesus' ministry of healing and teaching, the revelation broke through that he was this anointed one. When asked who Jesus was Peter confessed "You are the Christ" (Mark 8:29). The full weight of this confession, however, was not known until after the resurrection. Then Peter could say to the Jews, "Let all the House of Israel therefore know assuredly that God has made him both Lord and Christ, this Jesus whom you crucified" (Acts 2:36).

Several important points need to be considered as we think of the salvation brought through Christ.

1. Jesus came to do the will of God. The commitment made in the garden of Gethsemane indicates that Jesus had come to do the will of God (Matt. 26:36-39). He had asked that the cup of death be removed, but that was not to be. Thus, Jesus understood his own death to be the will of the Father. He saw his death as somehow being necessary and tried to communicate this understanding to the disciples (Mark 8:31; 9:31; 10:33-34).

In his obedience to God, Jesus represented the true Israel, fulfilling the prophetic word (Psa. 40:6-8) and bringing the perfect sacrifice of obedience to God.

2. *The will of God has to do with salvation.* Jesus indicated that he had come to seek and to save that which was lost (Luke 19:10), to give his life as a ransom for many (Mark 10:45). Jesus spoke of himself as the door of the sheepfold (John 10:9), as the good shepherd who lays down his life for the sheep (John 10:11). All this is true because Jesus has come that people may have life, and may have it in all its fullness (John 10:10).

3. *The salvation of God brings liberation.* Even as Israel was delivered from bondage, so we are freed from all captivities—from the "elemental spirits of the universe" (Gal. 4:3; Col. 2:15, 20). Paul says that all are justified by God's grace alone, through his act of liberation in the person of Jesus Christ (Rom. 3:24).

Salvation is spoken of in concrete historical terms. An actual historical bondage has been broken and a new liberty, a new freedom, a new life has come into being.

4. *Christ overcomes the powers of darkness.* Paul speaks of salvation as liberation from the powers of this world. "Principalities" and "powers" are those things that condition earthly life—those structures of life and society that hold people captive. Paul includes such things as life and death, governments, the law, traditions, human philosophies, feasts, astrology and angels (Rom. 8:38-39; 1 Cor. 15:24-26; Eph. 1:20-21; 3:10; 6:12; Col. 1:16; 2:15, 20).

These powers and structures are in themselves neither good nor evil; however, they can be used for either good or evil. But, the proclamation of the apostles is that in Jesus Christ the principalities and powers have been overcome and the reign of Jesus as Savior and Lord has begun. Here is salvation indeed—salvation that sets us free from all the powers that impinge upon our lives, keeping us from serving Christ.

Further Reflections

1. Salvation is real. It is an event; not only an inner emotion or attitude. Salvation is an event in history and has a "before" and an "after." Salvation is being freed from some real and concrete bondage or enslavement. It is an entering into a new relationship with God, who is recognized as the one who saves.

2. Salvation is inclusive. We noticed in the promise to Abraham that salvation was spoken of in terms of land, posterity, and provisions. In the Exodus event, salvation meant freedom from physical bondage, and more broadly salvation from all bondages that keep people from serving the living God. In Israel's subsequent history it is hard to separate the everyday sense of "save" and the spiritual or theological meaning of "save." When Israel was saved from her enemies, it was always understood as God's action of deliverance; God sent the "saviors" to his people (Gen. 45:7; Judges 3:9, 15; 2 Kings 13:5; Neh. 9:27). Thus every deliverance came from God and there was no "saving" apart from God. In Israel's understanding, it was impossible to separate the secular and the sacred elements of salvation. For a people whose lives are dedicated to God, all history is salvation history.

In the New Testament account of Jesus' birth, he is announced as coming to save the people from their sins. In his earthly ministry Jesus tells the paralytic that his sins are forgiven (Mark 2:1-12), and the adultrous woman to sin no more (John 8:3-11). But most of the time he heals the sick and casts out demons. All of these acts are seen as saving acts. Jesus saw and responded to the wholeness of each person. Salvation is all inclusive. It encompasses all of life.

3. Salvation is forward-looking and anticipatory. The fact that God had delivered them from past slavery assured Israel that God would deliver them in any present crises, as well as in the future. God saved; God is active in a saving way now; and God will save. All three need to be recognized and emphasized. To speak of God's saving only in terms of "having been saved" is to be unaware of God's saving work in the present. To speak of salvation as being only in the future is to deny God's power to save in the present. Salvation here and now receives its proper focus when

it is seen in relation to what God has done and will yet do in saving his people.

In our more traditional churches the emphasis has been on the future aspect of salvation; if we are faithful to the end we will be saved. In the more evangelical churches the emphasis has been on the past aspect of salvation; we have been saved. Biblically, however, they belong together. The past, present, and future aspects of salvation are one continuing work of God.

4. Salvation is ongoing. It is not a matter of once saved, always saved. Israel knew that God was at work in a saving way all the time. We also know this from our own experience. Though we have committed our lives to Christ and have been born again, we tend to fall into captivities from which we need to be freed. Even as Christians, we need to turn from the personal sins of rebellion and separation from God and find the freedom of new life in Christ.

Because there are "invisible orders of thrones, sovereignties, authorities, and powers" that contrive to bind us, and because Satan still seeks to hold us captive to tradition, laws, customs, fads, and fashions, we even now need to be saved. We need to be freed from all things which bind us and prevent us from serving Christ our Lord. Part of our need may be that we are so much a part of our culture that we are not even aware of our bondage. At such times, Christians from other nations and cultures may be able to help us recognize our enslavement.

As Christians we need to take more seriously the fact that Christ frees us from all principalities and powers. Where are we compromised to the culture and to the spirit of the times? How can we throw off these captivities? What are the structures that bind us? How can we bring basic Christian principles to bear on our jobs, our relationships, and the social and political structures of our day? As Christians, we need to look for and set up new models for just and liberated community living; we need to find a lifestyle that takes into account the world community.

5. Salvation calls for commitment. As we believe in God and commit ourselves in obedience to his will, we will come to know his will. The promise of salvation is given in Christ, but that promise cannot be experienced

O Lord, your gifts are
    prompted by your grace;
Your kingdom claims
    all nations and each race.
Lift up our hearts,
    and teach our tongues to share
This love of yours
    with people everywhere.

Then sing my friends, sing of love.
    Shout your joy in a jubilant
                        song,
For God has said "You are set
                        free"
    Sisters and brothers we can be
For time and for all eternity,
    So deep is God's love, so strong.

~Kenneth J. Morse

59

unless we commit our lives in faith and trust and obedience. In other words, salvation will change our life and our lifestyle!

6. The salvation offered in Christ is all encompassing. It includes personal salvation and the community of faith. It extends to all of history and to the universe. Salvation encompasses all of life—our physical, mental, emotional, and spiritual selves; salvation touches mind, body, soul, and spirit. Salvation results in a new life personally and it forms a new community of faith—the body of Christ.

7. Salvation is dynamic. It is much more than we often recognize. Salvation is not a theory or a set of ideas about God; it is not a set of doctrines which must be believed; it is not a philosophy of life, carefully worked out from experience; it is not a mystical absorption into the divine being. Salvation is an event in history, and in our lives, and it changes the course of history.

Thus the Bible is not concerned with speculations about salvation; the Bible *proclaims* salvation. Its concern is to make known the saving acts of God toward Israel and in Jesus Christ. This proclamation comes as a recital of, and a testimony to, what God has done. The events of the past, the Exodus, and the call of Christ, are thus seen as part of our history; and these events live on in those who have experienced the saving work of God.

8. Salvation looks forward to a time of ultimate fulfillment. This promise of salvation to come gives us hope for our work in the present. It informs our work of evangelism and missions. It provides the assurance of salvation in our present life and in our future.

God Invites Us

God, through the sending of his son, offers us an invitation to salvation. Jesus said that he came to seek and to save the lost: "Come to me, all who labor and are heavy laden, and I will give you rest" (Matt. 11:28). Jesus promised that whoever believes in him should not perish but have everlasting life (John 3:16). We know these promises; and they relate directly to the bondages that we experience. Through these promises, we are invited to faith and salvation.

60

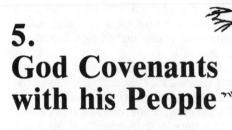

5.
God Covenants
with his People

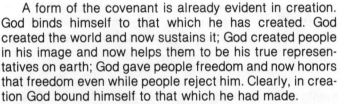

A form of the covenant is already evident in creation. God binds himself to that which he has created. God created the world and now sustains it; God created people in his image and now helps them to be his true representatives on earth; God gave people freedom and now honors that freedom even while people reject him. Clearly, in creation God bound himself to that which he had made.

The promise is also a form of the covenant. God held out a promise to Abraham, and in so doing bound himself to Abraham and his response of obedience and disobedience. The promise was unconditional, representing God's commitment and purposeful action which was not dependent on the people's faithfulness nor nullified by their unfaithfulness. It represented God's binding himself to his people.

The work of salvation contains an aspect of the fulfillment of promise and an aspect of covenant. It fulfilled the promise in that it saved the people for their service to God; it also expressed in concrete events what God covenanted or purposed to do.

God's revelations to Israel through the Exodus event led to the Sinai events, where the focus was God's covenant with Israel.

The Basis of the Covenant

The events and the divine revelations at Sinai are

reported in Exodus 19:1 to Numbers 10:10. Nowhere else in the Old Testament do we find such extended treatment of a single event. The various strands of this literature give testimony to one basic fact: at Sinai, God revealed to his people the binding ordinances which are basic for living life under God. At Sinai God made a covenant with his people. The centrality of this material points out its significance to Israel and to the church.

The Bible speaks of many kinds of covenants. They may be between individuals (Gen. 21:27; 26:28), between husband and wife (Mal. 2:14), between tribes (1 Sam. 11:1; Judg. 2:2; Exod. 23:32), between monarchs (1 Kings 20:34), between a king and the people (2 Kings 11:4), or even forced on the vanquished by a victorious king (1 Kings 20:34). Thus the idea of covenant relations was not new.

This covenant which God made with the people has many features which parallel the Hittite suzerainty treaty (which spelled out the mutual obligations between a ruler and a subject people). Distinguishing features of the covenant are these:

1. The preamble introduces the lord or sovereign who makes the covenant. In Exodus 20, the Ten Commandments are introduced simply as "I am the Lord your God." God himself establishes the covenant.

2. An historical introduction describes the previous relationships between the two parties. In the Decalogue (the Ten Commandments), this introduction is brief, but very basic: "I am the Lord your God who brought you out of the land of Egypt, out of the house of bondage" (Exod. 20:2). This saving action of God gives the basis for God's claim on their lives.

3. The prohibition against relating to other sovereign powers is stated. Israel is not to enter into an alliance with other monarchs. The Decalogue states clearly, "You shall not make for yourself any graven images . . . you shall not bow down to them or serve them" (Exod. 20:4-5). The relationship to God in the covenant is a jealous relationship and excludes the worship of other gods.

4. Provision for the deposit and public reading of the treaty is made. It is to be housed in the sanctuary and to be read in public. This provision is not found in the Decalogue

Three Lions

63

itself, but Deuteronomy 10:5 states that the tables of stone are to be placed in the Ark of the Covenant, a portable sanctuary. Provision for the public reading is found in Deuteronomy 31:10-11 and was later practiced by Ezra.

    5. *A list of witnesses is given.* In a suzerainty treaty, the gods of both parties would be named as well as important features of the natural world (mountains, rivers, etc.). In the Sinai Covenant, reference is made to the people (Josh. 24:22) and to stones (Josh. 24:27).

    6. *Blessings and curses are named.* A listing of benefits for obedience and calamities for disobedience is given in Deuteronomy 27—28; similar statements appear in the prophetic literature.

    From this listing of the features of the covenant, we can see that this is a binding covenant between God and the people. It is not a parity covenant (made between equals) nor is it a covenant in which God binds himself as in the covenant with Abraham (Gen. 15; 17) or David (2 Sam. 23:5). Rather, this is a covenant in which the people participate. They promise to do all that the Lord has commanded (Exod. 19:8); they acknowledge their own obligation to keep the law.

    The law functioned as the expression of the will of God. It called attention to the things which led to life and would bring God's blessing, and to the things which led to death and would bring God's judgment. The law was not a burden; it was a gift of God. Because of the law Israel could know and could do the will of God.

The Continuation of the Covenant

    The narrative in Joshua 24 continues almost all of the features of the covenant. A lengthy recital of God's gracious acts toward the patriarchs and to Moses is given. Reference is made to the Exodus, to the wilderness wanderings, to the entrance into the promised land. The acts of God are updated in this historical review; then the people are asked once more to renew the covenant.

    Joshua gives the invitation:

    "And if you be unwilling to serve the Lord, choose this day whom you will serve, whether the gods your fathers served in the region beyond the River, or the gods of the Amorites in whose land you dwell; but as for me and my house, we will serve the Lord" (Josh. 24:15).

This invitation is in the form of a covenant renewal, as well as being an open invitation for others to serve the living God. For the commitment to God needs to be made by each new generation and must be renewed or called to mind afresh in a public ceremony.

After a long period of kings had neglected the covenant tradition, Josiah made an attempt to return to the covenant when the law book was discovered in the temple (2 Kings 22). Josiah made a covenant with God to keep the commandments and statutes of the Lord (2 Kings 23:3); he enjoined the people to do the same (vv. 21-23). But this revival was short lived, as Josiah fell in battle at Meggido (v. 29).

In the time of Ezra, after the return from exile, another attempt was made to establish life under the covenant in Jerusalem. At a public convocation, the law was proclaimed and established with an oath and a curse (Neh. 10:29). The commitment now was not only to keep the laws of the covenant, but also to obey the accumulated tradition of interpretation that had been developed during the exile. The focus was on the commitment to the Torah or law; this became the basis on which a more legalistic approach to the law of Moses developed in Judaism.

Perhaps the most significant use of the covenant was made by the prophets just before and after the Babylonian captivity. They saw the covenant in relation to election—to God's choosing of a people. They saw the covenant as the working agreement between a sovereign Lord and his subject people, with the will of God being clearly indicated in the law.

On the basis of the covenant the prophets spoke: "Thus saith the Lord." On the basis of the covenant, the relationship between God and the people was described in terms of father/son (Hos. 11; Isa. 1:2); shepherd/flock (Isa. 40:11); potter/clay (Jer. 18); and husband/wife (Isa. 50:1; 54:5; Jer. 2:1-7; and Hosea). Israel's existence was always evaluated and understood in terms of election and covenant.

The covenant was also the basis for the prophets' noting how far Israel fell short of a true relationship with God. In fact they described this relationship as one of

65

rebellion—a rebellion openly displayed in the totality of life (Amos 3—4). Isaiah began his message with the word of God: "Sons have I reared . . . but they have rebelled against me" (Isa. 1:2). From their understanding of the covenant, the prophets proclaimed a judgment of exile, famine, and deprivation to the nation.

But even in the face of this rebellion against God, the prophets held out a message of hope to the people. God would not forsake his covenant, but would send judgments so that the people may return to him; God would bring them back to the land and again be their God and they his people. Jeremiah indicated that this will require not only the forgiveness of God, but also a new covenant:

"Behold the days are coming, says the Lord, when I will make a new covenant with the house of Israel and the house of Judah . . . I will put my law within them and I will write it upon their hearts; and I will be their God and they shall be my people" (Jer. 31:31-33).

It is this new covenant which Jesus established at the Last Supper. Taking the cup he said, "Drink of it, all of you; for this is my blood of the covenant, which is poured out for many for the forgiveness of sins" (Matt. 26:27-28). Jesus made possible a new relationship to God through forgiveness and through faith in him.

Paul speaks of this new covenant, claiming that God has qualified us "to be ministers of a new covenant, not in a written code but in the Spirit; for the written code kills, but the Spirit gives life" (2 Cor. 3:6). Paul makes direct reference to the fulfillment of Jeremiah's prophecy (Heb. 8:1-13). The old covenant looks to the new and is fulfilled in it.

Further Reflections

1. We cannot do without covenants. We rely on spoken and unspoken covenants in relationships with our parents, our spouses, our neighbors, and all other significant relationships. Any secure or established relationship is a binding or covenant relationship.

2. Covenant and freedom are inter-related. We are not really free until we bind ourselves to others. When there are no binding commitments, we have chaos, not freedom.

Only as musicians bind themselves to certain scales and forms, are they free to express themselves through music. Only through establishing covenants of acceptance and trust, can we relate to others without being threatened. Only through a covenant of trust and fidelity, do married couples remain free in their relations to each other and to other persons.

So it is in our relationship to God. We are not really free until we bind ourselves to God in Christ. Not to do so is to seek to be gods ourselves or to bind ourselves to idols, both of which enslave rather than free us. The Bible knows of no absolute freedom. It knows that true freedom comes only as we receive Christ as Lord, only as we bind ourselves to his will. This is a difficult truth to accept in an individualistically oriented culture. But God's Word promises that if we will bind ourselves to Christ and to his will, we will be free indeed.

3. Covenants need to be maintained and renewed. We often do not pay enough attention to this. Covenants are sometimes broken through moments of rebellion, but just as often through neglect. They cannot be simply taken for granted. They will either grow and be strengthened, or they will gradually disintegrate and die.

Where covenants are broken, restoration is achieved through forgiveness and a renewed commitment. The innocent must take the wrong of the other and forgive it. The guilty must accept the forgiveness offered and make a new commitment to the covenant.

Where a covenant has been neglected, it must be renewed and revitalized. Here we are often impatient. We expect a relationship that has been slowly deteriorating for years to be turned around without suffering or effort. What is needed, instead, is the thoughtful wooing of a renewed courtship.

4. Broken covenants result in judgments that are intended to lead us to repentance and to return to Christ. Yet we do little better than Israel in reading these judgments. God indicates through Amos, "I gave you cleanness of teeth in all your cities, and lack of bread in all your places, yet you did not return to me" (Amos 4:6). All the judgments God brought upon Israel were not enough to cause them to

repent (Amos 4:6-13), even though he desired that they should seek him and live (Amos 5:4-5).

The judging hand of God is seen in many areas of our lives and in our land. There is the cleavage between rich and poor, marriage breakdown, battered wives and children, consumerism that leads to greater emptiness, war and rumors of war, more subtle forms of compulsion, and more ways of taking advantage of others. If we had the eyes of an Amos we would know that we must re-orient our lives again to the covenant. God's judgment calls us to repentance, to faith, and to a new commitment to Christ, so that the principalities and powers of our day might indeed be overcome and we might be true to our covenant relationship to Christ.

5. A covenant relationship can remain vital only if there is growth in the relationship. Growth occurs when we hold out to others new vision or new promises. Where there is no growing edge in a relationship, it is hard to maintain even the outward form of a covenant. Perhaps this is why so many marriages fail today; couples have nothing more to offer each other by way of promise. Persons in their relationship may center too much on things and tasks and achievements, and not enough on being persons to each other.

Our commitment to God also cannot be taken for granted. Our commitments must be concrete acts which cost us something. We cannot simply claim to love God and not love a neighbor (1 John 4:20) or do wrong (1 John 3:10). Our commitment to God reaches into every area and aspect of life. Our covenant with God will remain fresh as we offer more and more of ourselves to God, and as we grow in our sensitivities to the presence of God in the world.

6. The prophets used justice and righteousness as criteria for evaluating Israel's covenant relationship. God's will, as expressed in the law, was that the people be just in all their relationships. Israel did not fare too well in this respect in the time of Amos. But how are we doing today?

Our covenant relationship will not be judged so much by our piety as by our deeds; our words of love will not say as much as our acts of mercy, kindness, and justice. We will be measured, not in comparison to our middleclass values, but in comparison to the poor.

7. Covenant keeping in Israel was the affair of the whole people; it was not a private or individual affair. The new covenant is also related to the community of faith, to the total body of Christ. Baptism is a commitment to Christ and a recognition of the fellowship of believers in which we live out the life of faith.

We have much growing to do to learn to be a covenanting church—to be a binding and loosing community. To be forgiven of God is to be forgiven in the community of faith (Matt. 6:14-15); to be sent out by God's spirit is to be sent out into service by the church (Acts. 13:1-4); to be freed from principalities and powers is to be freed to live a different life in church and society.

Whenever we, as a church, seek the will of God in some matter, and come to a decision which we feel to be the promise of God to us, then it is a binding word and we should hold each other to it. The decision becomes normative for the group. However, how often do we work through issues deeply enough that this binding, normative quality is reached? Much sacrifice and hard work is needed to become a loosing (liberating, saving) and binding fellowship.

God Invites Us

God not only made a covenant with Israel; God also established a new covenant in and through the work of Christ. God is ready to be in a covenant relationship with each one of us. But such relationship is not forced upon us. God does not override our personal choices and response. God offers forgiveness of our sins and the gift of his Spirit and invites us, through Christ, to respond in faith and follow.

6.
God Is Reigning

God is the reigning sovereign of all the world; this truth had already become clear to Israel in the Exodus event. In that event they knew God to be the sovereign Lord, the Creator and Sustainer of all things. God was Israel's leader. During and after the Exodus, God governed his people through Moses, Joshua, and other appointed leaders. But it was always clear that these leaders governed as God's representatives.

Kingship in Israel

The history of Israel's leadership moved through various phases—from early tribal leadership, through various stages of kingship, to the hope for God's eventual reign on earth. We will look more closely at these phases of leadership and the movement from one stage to another.

1. Tribal leadership. Once in the promised land, the Israelites lived under the leadership of tribal or clan chieftains. When one of the tribes was threatened in such a way that meant danger for all, charismatic leaders rallied the people in a united effort; together they overthrew the foes that threatened their land. These leaders were sent by God to accomplish specific tasks. In this early period of Israelite history, there were no political, administrative, or military structures which encompassed all of the tribes. They were bound together by their faith.

2. *The judges as leaders.* From the time of Moses on, judges exercised leadership in Israel. They had authority to administer justice by trying cases of law. Moses himself was such a judge; and Jethro advised him to appoint other judges to share the work (Exod. 18:13-27). Even the patriarchs administered justice in their own families (Gen. 21—22; 27). Though the judges were often military leaders who both delivered and governed the people, they were not connected with tribal government or kingship. In all cases they served God directly in their judgments.

An early attempt was made to introduce kingship through the system of judges. When Gideon judged the people and gained victory for them, they begged him to be king over them (Judg. 8:22), but he refused. His son, however, apparently felt that the throne then rightly belonged to him (Judg. 9:1-3). The reason Gideon refused the crown was because God is king; it is God who reigns (Judg. 8:23). All those who entered into covenant with God recognized God as their king (Deut. 33:5).

3. *The call for a king.* In spite of a clear recognition that God is the king, the trend toward an earthly king was not to be stopped. Israel was slowly changing from a semi-nomadic lifestyle to a more settled life on the land. The structures and institutions which governed in the earlier situation were giving way to structures more suited to the new situation.

As the people settled in different parts of the country, the leadership of the clan and tribal authorities slowly disintegrated. The constant threat of enemies created the need for better and more centralized political structures. For Israel to continue under the leadership of judges only meant that the enemy could easily enter and conquer. As the Philistine threat grew, the need for new governing structures became more obvious.

Israel was ambivalent about this need for a different form of leadership. The situation was desperate; it seemed to call for a new centralized government, for a king who could take charge and mobilize the people. Yet everyone in Israel knew that God alone was king. We read of this ambivalence in the biblical texts; we hear it expressed in Samuel. Samuel sees this call for a king as apostasy against God (1 Sam. 7—8); he calls for a return to God who will deliver Israel from the enemy. 1 Samuel 7:13 suggests that the Lord honored Samuel's cry and stayed the hands of the Philistines during Samuel's life.

4. The establishing of the monarchy. Nevertheless, God did ask Samuel to honor the wishes of the people and to anoint a king over Israel (1 Sam. 8:22). God permitted them to have a king, but indicated clearly what it would mean to have a king rule over them (1 Sam. 8:9-18). They would be conscripted and taxed to a tenth of their possessions, without mercy or regard for the individual. But the people still insisted on a king. So God gave them what they called for, together with all the consequences of such a new structure.

Samuel's anointing of Saul as king to reign over Israel (1 Sam. 10) and his anointing of David later (1 Sam. 16:1-13), indicates that the king should be a ruler under God, doing the will of God, and keeping his commandments. It was soon evident, however, that Saul had listened, not to God, but to the wishes of the people (1 Sam. 15:24); he was then replaced by David. The king was to rule as God's representative, not through his own might. The law of the covenant applied to the king as much as to the people.

5. A painful experience. From the beginning Israel's kings found it difficult to fully honor God as king. The power which they had been given tempted them to become absolute rulers. This was similar to Adam and Eve's temptation. The task given to these kings by God tempted them to take the place of God; the temptation was to become absolute monarchs and to throw off their role as sons and servants of God.

6. God's covenant with David. David, though he sinned before God, was nevertheless seen as a man of God who had done what was right in the sight of God. He united the north and the south; he centralized the worship of Israel by bringing the Ark of the Covenant to Jerusalem and building a house of cedar for it (2 Sam. 7).

God honored the reign of David by giving to him an everlasting covenant (2 Sam. 7:8-17; 23:5; Jer. 33:20-21). Thus, the covenant with Israel was now specifically

Three Lions

73

confirmed, with David as the representative of the people. This covenant, similar to the promise made to Abraham, was unconditional. It became the basis for hope when Israel could no longer see hope for life on earth. In the darkest moments of their history, Israel knew that God had promised; God had made a covenant and God would keep his covenant with his people.

7. *The promise of a Messiah.* The history of the kings is a sad one because only a few kings did what was pleasing to God. So the thoughts and longings of the people turned more and more toward the future; they looked forward to the time when God would fulfill his promise to David of a righteous king and a reign of justice and equity. The people looked more and more to the King-Savior, the Lord's anointed, who would bring in the reign of God once again. Thus, out of their experience of kingship came the expectation of a Messiah (Isa. 9:6-7; 11:1-5; Micah 5:2-5; Jer. 23:5-6; Ezek. 37:24-25).

8. *Hope in dark days.* During the historical period between the Old Testament and the New Testament, things looked hopeful for a while. The people had returned to the land; they had rebuilt the temple and the city walls; they had their own leaders to rule over them. But when the Persian and Egyptian rule ended, and the rule of Antiochus 4th of Syria began (175 B.C.), the people's hope again was that God would break into history and set up his reign on earth. Only in this way could equity and justice be gained. The people could not see how any ruler in Israel would be able to throw off the yoke of bondage to other nations. God would have to intervene directly to keep his promise to David.

Christ is King

The people waited for the revelation of God to come with power and set free those who trusted in God's promises. At Jesus' birth the announcement was given that he would be the saviour of the people; he would save the people from their sins (Matt. 1:21). Jesus was seen as fulfilling the promise to David:

He will be great and will be called the Son of the Most High; and the Lord God will give to him the throne of his father David, and he will reign over the house of Jacob forever; and of his kingdom there will be no end (Luke 1:32-33).

Jesus' coming was understood as having political and social implications as well:

He has shown strength with his arm, he has scattered the proud in the imagination of their hearts, he has put down the mighty from their thrones, and exalted those of low degree; he has filled the hungry with good things, and the rich he has sent empty away (Luke 1:51-54).

When Jesus entered his public ministry, he referred to his mission in terms of the kingdom or the reign of God. "The time is fulfilled, and the kingdom of God is at hand; repent, and believe in the gospel" (Mark 1:15). He interpreted the significance of his work of casting out demons in terms of the kingdom. "But if it is by the finger of God that I cast out demons, then the kingdom of God has come upon you" (Luke 11:20). It is clear that Jesus came to inaugurate the reign of God on earth. He came to do the will of God and he asked others to follow him. As Jesus lived out the will of God, the reign of God became visible for others to see.

During Jesus' earthly ministry, the people could not fully reconcile his teachings and life with their expectations and hopes for the coming Day of the Lord. Some believed and some did not. Those who were with Jesus and trusted in him did come to understand that he was in truth the Messiah, the anointed of God (Mark 8:27-30); yet even they did not fully understand the Messiah to be the suffering servant, needing to go the way of the cross.

Further Reflections

1. Structures that have served well at one time may need changing in new situations. Seen in this way, structures are not sacred—they are servants. People in their creativity call structures into being. Structures are ways of ordering the world, of overcoming chaotic situations, of achieving specific goals and ends. Thus as their life situation changed, Israel changed from judges to kings.

The making of such changes does not condemn the previous structure or way of doing things. The former way was probably as appropriate in its time as a new way is now. How and when can we understand such change as a positive step, rather than a negative one?

2. New structures are usually called into being when old ones no longer function adequately. Thus when Samuel's sons began to misuse the office of judge, the people clamored for a king (1 Sam. 8:1-5). As long as people have the freedom of choice, no structure is free from misuse, free from sin. The more a structure is misused, the more chaos is created; and this calls for a new ordering, a new structuring that will be just and equitable.

Seen in this way, the creating of new structures is one way in which people are co-creators with God; we can help establish new possibilities for life and for fullness of life (shalom).

3. No structure is a guarantee of justice and equity, but some present fewer temptations to evil than others. It is possible to be Christian in all structures; but some tend toward corruption to such a degree that a warning must be given. So it was in the time of Samuel. He was instructed to tell the people about the weaknesses of kingly rule; he warned them of the toll it would take on the lives of the people.

Apply this same principle today. We live in a capitalistic economic structure. We are Christians in it. But are the opportunities for serving our own ends so great in this structure that we could lose our Christian witness and power? What toll might it take in our lives?

4. It is possible to be Christian in many different kinds of structures. It is possible to live a Christian life under a democracy, under a monarchy, or under a socialist or communist structure. It is not the structure that makes us Christians, but whom we serve.

Though it is possible to be Christian under any structure, it is not always possible to do so without suffering or martyrdom. Jesus did the will of God, but was crucified. Many martyrs have followed his example. We cannot do without a theology of suffering if we want to be Christian in the world.

5. It is not possible to live without structures. To remove or demolish one structure immediately invites another to take its place. We cannot simply be negative

about structures; we need them. Life would return to chaos if it were not for some form of ordering our lives.

6. There are no perfect structures, because it is not the structures in themselves that are good or bad as a rule. The problem comes in the way we use those structures.

Take Robert's Rules of Order. This structure is designed to help us make decisions in an orderly and just way. But who has not seen those same rules used on a conference floor to defeat a motion, not by a vote, but by amendments that nullify the motion. The rules aren't the problem; rather the ends to which we put them need to be questioned.

As long as people choose to sin there will be no perfect economic, political, educational, or church structure. So our task is to evaluate such structures, to seek to make them more just and equitable. Our task is to get people to use the structures for good and not for evil. For this to happen, we need to be open to change, both in society and in the church.

7. When we model new structures, new ways of achieving our goals and purposes, they come under God's permissive will. God permits us to re-order things, just as he permitted kingship in Israel. These new models may bring with them new evils that we have not foreseen; and that may actually offset the good we had hoped to accomplish. But God permits us to re-order life according to our own interests and objectives and our best understandings. God allows us to structure things anew.

Many areas of life need the modeling of new structures: ways of overcoming our individualistic style of life; new and simpler lifestyles altogether; new ways of bringing justice to the laborers; and new patterns of family life to overcome the problems created by the nuclear family.

It is important when modeling these new structures to monitor them closely. We need to see whether there are any signs of God's blessing or judgment on the new venture. Is it in fact accomplishing what it was intended to do?

8. The actual modeling of new structures happens in our families and in the community of faith. As we become more sensitive to God's purposes of love and justice for all, and as we notice that these ends are frustrated or are impossible to achieve through present structures, we call new

structures into being. In the past the church has modeled better ways of health care, education, and prison reform. Our own churches have modeled voluntary service, Pax, Heifer Project, disaster services, and other ways of meeting human need. Yet much more can be done and needs to be done.

9. The judges were charismatic rulers. They were called of God and empowered to act in times of crises to deliver the people from impending danger. Later, the prophets were called in a similar way. They were called to address particular evils, but they did not have an ongoing office. This tells us that God is not tied to institutionalized leadership. Where the structures have become so well engrained so as to completely control people's lives, God sends charismatic leaders to break us out of the mold and give us new life again. In this way God overcomes structures that have become binding or enslaving principalities and powers. Nevertheless, the new life that results will receive a structure of its own and it may have elements in it that are no better than the old.

10. The reign of God continues, even into our own time. God was active through Moses, Joshua, and the judges to lead his people. God was also with David and those kings who were open to do his will. The form of leadership changed, but God was still King.

The monarchy as a power structure had such a strong tendency towards corruption and misuse of power that it was a painful way to learn that in truth only God is King. However, the lesson Israel learned from the monarchy was important: Everything that their kings were not (merciful, peace loving, just, and righteous), the coming Messiah would be and would bring about. The time of the kings made the people aware of a new kingdom, a coming reign of God that would be one of peace and justice for all.

The reign of God is present in our own time. God functions in and through the institutions of our day. God has not left humanity to itself, even though at times we choose forms of ordering life that are not the best. God is active in communist societies and capitalist societies, in democracies and military dictatorships, in churches with congregational polity and churches with episcopal polity. In all areas of life God is at work seeking to accomplish his purpose and goal in history.

God Invites Us

In every structure, in every age, God invites people to do his will. And wherever God's will is done, there his reign is in power. What a way to evangelize! As we invite people to give themselves to Christ and to do his will, the reign of God is being established. As we become aware of God's purposes and respond to them in obedience, God's reign takes shape in our midst.

7.
God Is Speaking

The prophets and prophetic ministry form a very unique function in Israel's history. Yet prophecy was not isolated from the rest of Israel's life. We can see evidence of this interrelatedness in the Hebrew scriptures. They were divided into three parts—the Law (Pentateuch), the Prophets, and the Writings (wisdom). And yet all three form the larger whole; thus we will seek to discover how the function of prophecy is related to the priestly and to the wisdom aspects of Israel's life.

The Nature of the Prophetic Ministry

To understand the nature of prophetic ministry, we will consider the relationship between (1) prophet and priest, and (2) prophet and sage.

1. Prophet and Priest. Prophecy shares with the priestly (or legal) tradition an emphasis on divine revelation. From both prophet and priest, we hear the word of God spoken in the first person. The priests held before the people the word of God which related to what was generally significant in their lives. Priests upheld the regulations and observances which the people must follow to abide by God's revelation given in the past. Priests upheld the law and the traditions which were a part of the people's normal life and practice. These included regulations and traditions related to worship, sacrifice, interpretation of Scripture, and teaching.

80

The prophet, on the other hand, spoke of the revelation of God as it related to specific situations and circumstances; the prophet addressed situations where it was hard to know exactly what was of God and what was idolatry or disobedience to God. For example, the priest's concern would be that appropriate sacrifices were made for offenses, transgressions, or thanksgivings. The prophet's concern was to speak out when these practices became a lie and a hoax rather than being a true expression of faith.

So we see how closely the prophetic role and the priestly function were connected. The content of the prophet's message complemented the priest's function. The priestly message did not require a constantly new revelation; the revelation had already been given in the law. But at times the application of that message to a changed or new situation needed the new insight and revelation of the prophet. The priestly tradition rested on the mediation of the law and covenant as revealed to Moses—on the Torah. The prophet was also sensitive to God's will and purpose as expressed in this law; but the prophet moved further, focusing on whether the people were actually abiding by this revealed word. Thus the prophet brought additional insight from God to specific situations.

At times we have understood the prophet as being totally opposed to the priestly functions; that, however, is to misunderstand the nature of both prophet and priest. The prophetic word was strongly based on the law and the covenant.

2. *Prophet and Sage.* In a similar way the prophetic word and the word of the sage are closely related. The word of wisdom, however, is often given in the third person; it is a common-sense way of speaking. The wisdom literature comes from careful and long-standing observations about how God works in the world. Such wisdom literature is found in Job and Proverbs especially, but also in the Psalms and the prophetic writings.

The prophet did not negate this approach to life; rather, he took it very much for granted. The prophetic voice spoke up when people's actions were absurd, non-rational, or unwise; the prophet invited them to think again about what they were doing. So the prophet did not bypass human reasoning. Rather, he exposed situations in which people had so rationalized their behavior that they believed they were doing the will of God when they were in fact in disobedience to God's will. The prophet exposed situations where human reason had led people astray. For example, Israel thought that because they were God's people the Day of the Lord would be a blessing to them. Amos let them know that this reasoning was false, that they would in fact receive judgment rather than blessing.

The Functions of the Prophet

For a clearer understanding of prophetic work, we will look at three basic functions of the prophet.

1. The prophets were God's spokesmen. They received a personal and specific call from God (Exod. 3:1—4:17; Isa. 6; Jer. 1:4-19; Hos. 1:2; Amos 7:14-15), whereas the false prophets took the office upon themselves (Jer. 14:14). God's prophets were called to proclaim a message to the people.

2. The prophets became the interpreters of the covenant to the people. They were keenly aware of the purposes God was pursuing with his people; they saw how the disobedience and rebellion of the people thwarted these purposes. And they pointed the people to a renewed observance of the covenant. They stood in the midst of the events of their day and saw in them the character and purposes of God; they observed whether God was acting in terms of blessing or judgment.

As the prophetic understanding of God's unfolding purposes deepened, the prophets spoke to every aspect of Israel's life that stood in the way of God's full and complete rule. They spoke against Israel's leaders. They charged the priests with failing to follow and teach God's word, with being too anxious for their pay (Hos. 4:6-8; Mic. 3:11; Zeph. 3:4). They even accused the prophets of violating their calling (Jer. 23:16, 26; Isa. 28:7; Mic. 3:5). The prophets also charged other persons and groups with wrongdoing: the merchants for stealing (Amos 8:4-6; Hos. 12:7-8); the city women for their luxury (Amos 4:1; Isa. 3:16-17); and all persons for the various immoralities they practiced (Psa. 53:3).

All of these charges were not simply repetitions of the laws of the covenant. Rather, they were interpretations of the people's acts, made on the basis of their covenant relationship. For example, the law said, "Thou shalt not steal" (Exod. 20:15); the prophet's interpretation said: "What you are doing in taking a bribe is actually stealing" (Amos 5:10-13), even though the people thought their action was justified. So the law of the covenant was basic; to specifically speak to current practices was the prophet's task.

The prophets also spoke to political and national affairs. They were not slow in confronting kings and governors, using a style patterned after Moses' confrontation with Pharaoh. The prophets criticized political leaders for ignoring basic morality, for accepting bribes, for exploiting the weak and the poor (Amos 6:1-6; Hos. 5:10; 7:3; Isa. 1:23; 3:14; Mic. 3:1-3, 9-11). The kings knew the law, but they needed reminding that their present actions did not fulfill the law.

3. The function of the prophets was also one of forthtelling and foretelling, of proclamation and prophecy. No hard line can be drawn between prophecy as forthtelling and prophecy as foretelling; even telling what God's future course of action will be if there is no repentance is a foretelling of events. It is impossible to declare the will and purposes of God without reference to the future. In this sense all prophecy is oriented to the future. Where the prophets promise either blessing or judgment, this refers to what God will do in establishing his rule on earth. Even the false prophet was judged on the basis of whether his prophesies would come true (Jer. 28:9; Deut. 18:22).

This interpretation or proclamation of what God is doing and will yet do, is again based on the covenant and on the promises of God to Israel. The revelation to Israel through Moses remains basic in all prophetic proclamation.

The Message of the Prophets
Let's look more specifically now at the message the prophets spoke to the people of Israel. Several themes highlight this message.

1. The prophets spelled out very clearly the meaning of

the covenant and the sovereignty of God for the everyday life of the people. Naming God as Lord meant that all nations must answer to God for the crimes committed against humanity—crimes committed in war, through slave trade, or through the people's neglect of the law (Amos 1:3—2:16). God is the Lord of all that was created, of all of nature (Job 38—41). God is creator and sustainer of the universe (Psa. 24).

2. The prophets emphasized God's righteousness, and declared that nothing less than this was expected from God's people. Because God is righteous he seeks justice in all the earth. Thus the prophets became spokesmen in the area of ethics and social concerns. As we have noted, no problems escaped the prophet's voice: idolatry, sacred prostitution, (Hos. 4:14); sabbath violations; disrespect for parents (Mic. 7:6); murder; adultery; theft; covetousness; drunkenness; charging interest on loans (Ezek. 22:12); incest; and many more crimes against God and people. Thus the prophets not only proclaimed God's righteousness; they also stated the implications of God's righteousness. They spelled out in detail what such justice meant for Israel's lifestyle and showed how it was being trodden underfoot.

3. The prophets lifted up the judgment of God as a very present reality of life. Since God is king, God is also the judge (Gen. 18:25). The prophets saw that evil brought its own reward; this was inescapable (Prov. 14:34). Yet they did not simply call attention to God's judgments; they also named the purposes that God sought to achieve through such judgments. Amos 4:6-12 indicates that God has sent judgments of famine, drought, and sickness, so that the people would repent. Throughout the prophetic message, God's judgment is seen as a strong invitation to repent, to return to God; judgment is seen as a part of God's saving work.

4. The focus of the message of the prophets increasingly falls on the coming Day of the Lord. The more precarious the reign of Israel's historical kings became, the more they looked to a future intervention by God. They anticipated God's establishing of a new reign, bringing his enemies into subjection (Isa. 29:5-6). This would be a day of

blessing and judgment: blessing for those who were obedient to the covenant and judgment for the evildoers. The people of Israel largely believed this would be a day of rejoicing for them; the prophets, however, reminded them that even for Israel it would be a day of judgment (Amos 2:9-16).

The Day of the Lord was seen as God's decisive intervention in history; in this day God's kingly rule would be established. God would redeem his people and bring his purposes to completion. This hope was expressed in various ways: the overthrow of Babylon and the restoration of Israel (Isa. 13:1—14:23); the rejuvenation of creation after judgment (Isa. 34—35); a new exodus deliverance and the establishment of God's reign (Isa. 40—66); the final battle with God's enemies (Zech. 14); cosmic and earthly cataclysmic events, and the outpouring of God's Spirit on his people (Joel).

Several verses indicate times when the Day of the Lord occurred in the past. The Fall of Jerusalem was seen as such a day, as a day of God's fierce anger (Lam. 1;2). The defeat at Carchemish was also such a day for Egypt (Jer. 46:2-12). Thus, Israel understood that there had been various "Days of the Lord" and knew that there would be others. God's coming in specific events of blessing or judgment was a reality; and many of these events are yet to be, in the future.

The prophets' vision of what would happen on the Day of the Lord was not all fulfilled at one time. A part of this vision was fulfilled in Jesus' coming; other parts will be fulfilled at his Second Coming. Jesus himself, in quoting Isaiah 61:1-2, places a period in the middle of verse two, saying in effect that this has now been fulfilled; the rest (judgment) will come later.

"The Spirit of the Lord is upon me,
because he has anointed me to preach good news
 to the poor.
He has sent me to proclaim release to the captives
and recovering of sight to the blind,
to set at liberty those who are oppressed,
to proclaim the acceptable year of the Lord."

Luke 4:18-19

This indicates that the Day of the Lord is always present where God comes to bless and to judge his people.

Further Reflections

1. The prophetic ministry is much needed today. Christians need to speak, very specifically and from a Christian perspective, to the events, structures, and movements of our time. We need to address instances where the form, but not the reality, of laws, mores, or traditions is being kept. We need to address those areas of our lives which are compromised to the world, but which we have rationalized as being Christian.

When we are comfortable with our North American lifestyle, is it because we have rationalized ourselves into thinking it is okay? Is it perhaps at times a rebellion against the Lordship of Christ? Does our participation in the social, political, economic, and educational structure of society express obedience to God or rebellion against God? To answer such questions, we need the vision of the prophet.

If we try to avoid such specific application of the Word to our personal lives and to our culture, we make null and void the Word of God itself. It would remain a generality, finding no application in life. We need not only to know *that* we ought to love one another; we also need to know what is included in loving each other.

2. The prophetic ministry relates to both law and wisdom. It knows that the Christian faith has spelled out specific norms and expectations (law) for our relations with people. These we know from the Scriptures. The prophetic ministry also knows the truths (wisdom) that come to us from various disciplines of study. It accepts the values, goals, purposes, norms, and factual information which comes from observation of the world about us. Thus the prophetic word can speak clearly to specific aspects of our life and culture.

Sometimes this application results in a critical word and sometimes in a promising word. The difference lies in the situation of the hearer. If the hearer is in bondage or is oppressed, it comes as a word of promise; if the hearer is the oppressor, it comes as a word of judgment.

3. The prophetic word is an eschatological word—it

And what does the Lord
require of you
but to do justice,
and to love kindness,
and to walk humbly
with your God?

Micah 6:8

speaks about the future. It interprets the present on the basis of the past and the future. The prophetic word notes how God has already acted to judge and to bless, and it projects this upon our present acts. It looks at God's purposes in creation and in his dealings with humankind; it sees in these purposes the end that God has in mind for all people. By observing carefully what God has blessed and will bless, what God has judged and will judge, a word can be given for the present. It is both a word of warning and an invitation to faith. It is a prophetic word.

4. To live acceptably before God, our faith must be manifested in what we do. A true faith in God changes our lives towards greater righteousness. If we confess Christ, then people can expect us to be upright and honest in our dealings, loving and kind and helpful in our relationships, and self-sacrificing in our lifestyle. The prophets were concerned about the poor and the oppressed; they expected justice and sharing from God's covenant people. How could anything less be expected of us?

5. We need to discern more clearly what God is saying to our own culture and time. Remember how the word of judgment was given first to all the nations around Israel, including Judah; and then the message of God finally zeroed in on Israel—they would be judged more severely because they had received the greater knowledge of what God desired. Similarly, it may be easy for us to see that God will punish other peoples or nations, yet hard to realize that our own nations will be judged for sins against the peoples of the world. How will the prophetic word be heard by us in our situations? How does it deal with the specifics of our lives?

6. The prophetic word now has an even wider ministry than it had in Old Testament days. The prophets in the Old Testament spoke largely to their own people. But in the New Testament, the message of the gospel is clearly for *all* people. As Christians we have received a fuller revelation of God's word and will than the Old Testament prophets had. As a result our task is to proclaim what God has done and will do in the world. The prophetic message of today holds out the hope of the Day of the Lord, a day of promise and a day of judgment.

God Invites Us

Few people can tolerate the prophet who exposes our efforts to cover up disobedience with acceptable expressions of piety, our rationalizations of present lifestyles. A prophet is not a comfortable person to have around and is often rejected as Jesus indicated he would be.

But through the prophet's message comes our invitation to faith. We are invited to stop and see if what the prophet is saying is indeed true. Through the prophetic message, God invites us to confess our sins and to change our ways. We are invited to accept the revelation of God in Christ, to follow him, and to do his will.

8.
Jesus Is Lord

The first and basic confession of the early church was, "Jesus is Lord." To the Jews, these early Christians testified:

> This Jesus, delivered up according to the definite plan and foreknowledge of God, you crucified and killed by the hands of lawless men. But God raised him up . . . Let the house of Israel therefore know assuredly that God has made him both Lord and Christ, this Jesus whom you crucified (Acts 2:23-24, 36).

The confession that Jesus is both Lord and Christ says a great deal in this context. When the early church called Jesus "Christ," it meant they saw him as the anointed of God, the Messiah. They confessed that he was the one all Israel had been waiting for, the one who would fulfill the promises of God to his people. When early Christians called Jesus "Lord," they were acknowledging him to be one with God and therefore sovereign Lord over all the earth.

The theme of promise and fulfillment is clearly acknowledged in this basic confession. Jesus was recognized as the one who was to come, the one Moses pointed to (Deut. 18:15), the one Isaiah and Malachi spoke of (Isa. 40:3; Mal. 3:1-4). The early Christians recognized that Jesus was doing the work of God on earth, that Jesus continued the work God had begun with his people.

Jesus Christ—God become Man

Jesus is both divine and human. He shows God's love and power as a flesh-and-blood human being. Because he is divine, Jesus shows us who God is more clearly and more personally than any other person, word, or event. Because he is human, Jesus shows us what we ought to be. Jesus is a sign that God is in the midst of human life.

Jesus Christ—Revolutionary

Jesus comes on strong. He hits hard at phony religion and at narrow-mindedness. He seeks justice for the helpless and the abused. He expresses more concern for persons than for traditions and institutions. This revolutionary Jesus speaks and acts like an Old Testament prophet because he is moved by tenderness and compassion.

One With the Creator

This confession, "Jesus is Lord," recognizes that Jesus is one with the Creator. He was with God from the beginning:

> In the beginning was the Word, and the Word was with God, and the Word was God. He was in the beginning with God; all things were made through him, and without him was not anything made that was made (John 1:1-3).

It was not that easy to draw this conclusion about a man who had walked with them in Galilee. Just as the belief in God as Creator came to Israel through God's mighty acts of liberation, so belief in Christ as active in creation came through the people's experience of Christ's saving power.

Jesus Christ—Sufferer

Jesus' suffering is a message about the depth of God's desire to heal the broken relationships between people and God. The death of Jesus on the cross is a sign that at every moment in history God wants people to be in relationship with him. The cross helps us understand how much God suffers when we reject the invitation to relationship.

Jesus Christ—Liberator

Jesus frees us for life in the world. He proclaims a faith which frees from fear and hurt, which accepts crisis, change, challenge, and confrontation as part of life. Jesus proclaims a faith in the God who is alive and acting and surprising people. This liberating Jesus makes us aware that God laughs through his creation and wants to laugh within us.

The people recognized that Jesus had given them new life. Paul spoke of this in terms of a creative act, for "if any one is in Christ, he is a new creation; the old has passed away, behold the new has come" (2 Cor. 5:17). Bringing new life into being is a creative act; the people had experienced this in Christ. Jesus had himself said "unless one is born anew, he cannot see the kingdom of God" (John 3:3); people had personally experienced and continued to experience this new birth.

The disciples and others had also witnessed Jesus' power to still the storm, to heal the sick, and to cast out demons. They had to ask whether his power was of God or of Satan (Mark 3:20-22). And these experiences made sense only as they recognized Jesus as Creator and Lord.

They recognized in Jesus one who was, more than any human, co-creator with God. He was the true representative of God on earth. He was God incarnate, for "the Word became flesh and dwelt among us, full of grace and truth" (John 1:14).

Fulfillment of the Promises

Jesus fulfilled the promises of God to Israel; Jesus also continues the work of God in speaking his promises to us today. Paul was careful to explain that the promise to Abraham preceded the law, and therefore the law could not annul the promise (Gal. 3:6-29). Thus salvation came to Abraham through his faith in the promises; and salvation comes to us in the same way. Paul concludes: "if you are Christ's, then you are Abraham's offspring, heirs according to the promise" (Gal. 3:29).

At his birth it was prophesied that Jesus would "perform the mercy promised to our fathers" and would fulfill the promise of salvation so that people might serve him without fear (Luke 1:72-73; Acts 13:33; Rom. 1:1-2). It was clear to the early Christians that "The promise to Abraham and his descendants, that they should inherit the world, did not come through the law but through the righteousness of faith" (Rom. 4:13).

The work of Christ was seen throughout the New Testament as the fulfillment of God's promise to Abraham and to Israel. The fact that Gentiles now shared the life in the Spirit was a clear sign that the promise of a blessing to all nations through Abraham was being fulfilled (Eph. 3:6). All had become sons of Abraham, children of the promise, just as Isaac was.

Jesus also came with his own promises, continuing the work of God. He promised "Follow me, and I will make you fishers of men" (Mark 1:16-17). Even the form of the promise was like the promise to Abraham. In both cases, there was a command and then a promise.

People followed Jesus because they saw in him the promise of a new life, the promise of being accepted with forgiveness rather than condemnation, the promise of a righteous rule and of salvation. The same promise is held out to us today, whenever we read or hear the gospel story.

For all who believe, Jesus holds out the promise of the resurrection and of life beyond death. Thus our walk even now is informed by his promise to return and to establish his righteous rule.

Jesus as Savior

Jesus is Savior. He continues God's saving work; he continues to set at liberty those who are captive. In the synagogue at Nazareth, Jesus referred to himself as a savior. Quoting from Isaiah 61 he says: "The Spirit of the Lord is upon me, because he has anointed me to preach good news to the poor. He has sent me to proclaim release to the captives and recovering of sight to the blind, to set at liberty those who are oppressed, to proclaim the accept-able year of the Lord" (Luke 4:18-19). This is not only a fulfillment of prophecy; it also indicates that the saving, liberating work of God begun at the Exodus continues in Jesus. He frees people from bondage to sin and calls them to follow him in newness of life.

Jesus declared that he had come to seek and to save that which was lost (Luke 19:10). He came as a servant giv-ing his life as a ransom for many (Mark 10:45); that is, he gave up his life so that we might be free to live in him.

The early Christians experienced salvation through Christ on many levels. There was personal salvation. They were born again and received the spirit of Christ. They were new creatures in him; they thought new thoughts and dreamed new dreams as the prophets had said they would (Acts 2:14-21). They were freed from the power of sin and death and empowered by the Spirit to live a life of love and service to others. Paul beautifully characterized this new life: "I have been crucified with Christ; it is no longer I who live, but Christ who lives in me; and the life I now live in the flesh I live by faith in the Son of God, who loved me and gave himself for me" (Gal. 2:20).

This salvation also touched and transformed the Chris-tian's relationships with others. The wall of enmity between Jews and Gentiles was broken down (Eph. 2:13-14). This was not only a change in attitude, but also a change of social practices and tradition. Circumcised and uncircum-cised could eat and fellowship together, for circumcision was no longer mandatory. Slaves were held to be morally accountable on a level with their masters (Eph. 6:5-9). Women were morally accountable and seen as joint heirs in Christ, responsible for making their own decisions of faith (1 Pet. 3:1-7). Making these changes in relationships meant that the whole society was changed. Paul stated it succinctly: "There is neither Jew nor Greek, there is neither slave nor free, there is neither male nor female; for you are all one in Christ Jesus" (Gal. 3:28).

Jesus also called a whole new society into being. Those who were his constituted a new community, the Body of Christ. In this new community people modelled the new humanity, the new life that had come about through salvation in Christ. Wherever a vital faith in Christ is present, the church still serves as the community that models a new way of life to the world—a community transformed by the salvation of Christ and the Spirit of his love.

Thus Christ's saving power brought about changes in society as the relationships between people changed. And Christ's work also saved from the "principalities and powers." This refers to powers that are operative in the world, but not necessarily seen with the eyes: powers of greed, powers of ideologies, of custom and tradition, powers of astrology, powers of law. The early church knew that "we are not contending against flesh and blood, but against principalities, against the powers, against the rulers of this present darkness, against the spiritual hosts of wickedness in the heavenly places" (Eph. 6:12). But their confession was clearly that Jesus had saved them from these powers. Such principalities and powers had no hold on the early Christians any more. They were free to serve Christ. In the same way today, Christians experience Jesus' salvation as they are freed from captivity to the powers and structures of our society—structures over which we have no direct control, but which tend to shape and determine our lives.

The New Testament declares that in Jesus Christ the true salvation of God had come. This salvation had been pointed to in the Old Testament; now it is realized and fulfilled in Christ. The institution of sacrifice can now fall away. It had served well as it pointed to Christ; it had served to cover sin from year to year so that the power of sin would not work itself out amongst the people (Heb. 9:11-14). But now Christ has atoned for sin; it has been forgiven and can no longer stand in the way of the believer's fellowship with God.

The New Covenant

Jesus establishes the new covenant that Jeremiah spoke about. This covenant is based on better promises (Heb. 8:6); thus it fulfills as well as replaces the first covenant (Heb. 8:13). The work of Christ, his death for sinful humanity, is also seen as covering the transgressions of the first covenant (Heb. 9:15).

In this new covenant Jeremiah's prophecy is fulfilled. As the people receive the Spirit of God, the law is written on their hearts (Heb. 8:10); their knowledge of God is mediated through the Spirit, not through the careful teaching of a tradition received from the fathers (Heb. 8:11).

It is this new covenant of fellowship with Christ and his people that is celebrated in communion (Matt. 26:26-29). In the church, the Body of Christ, this covenant becomes visible for the world to see.

Jesus also fulfills the law. That is to say, he takes the place of the law. The law was given so that the people might know the will of God; it pointed to God's will for their lives. Jesus came to *do* the will of God and showed in his life what it means to live in ways acceptable to God. He demonstrated in his life what it meant to serve God better than any law could express it in words. Jesus calls us to follow him, to be his disciples, to learn from him what the will of God is for us.

The Coming of the Kingdom

God made the promise of an everlasting kingdom to David. In subsequent years, especially when the people were in bondage, Israel longed for a descendant of David who would come to usher in the kingdom of peace and righteousness, justice and prosperity. They waited many long years, always believing that God would honor the covenant made with David and establish his rule over his people.

During the inter-testamental period there were various speculations and beliefs about how God would bring in his reign. The system of interpretation developed by the scribes assumed that the kingdom of God would come when Israel perfectly kept the law and the tradition (both the written and the unwritten word); the Essenes called for a life of ritual cleanness and separation from the defilements of the world (as evidenced in the Qumran community); the Sadducees believed that the hope of Israel rested in the temple and its worship; the Zealots looked for the kingdom to begin through revolution and insurrection. The more apocalyptic interpretations felt that God himself would break into history with his hosts (army) to blot out all evil and set up his kingdom. All of these groups were preoccupied with the coming reign of God. It mattered very much to them that somehow God would usher in his reign. After all, this was what God had promised, and they knew God to be faithful to his word.

Jesus came announcing the inbreaking of the kingdom (Mark 1:15). His parables teach about the kingdom. He indicates that the kingdom has come in him (Mark 1:14-15), that it is present in their midst (Luke 7:20-21), and that it will come. The kingdom as Jesus talks of it is past, present, and future.

More specifically, since the reign of God is present wherever God's will is done, and since Jesus gave himself fully to the will of God, the nature of kingdom living can best be seen in Jesus. Jesus represents the life that humankind was to live. Jesus is the true representative of God, for he is the image and likeness of God in the flesh (Heb. 1:2-3).

It is not surprising, therefore, that Jesus calls those who believe in him to follow him and to become his disciples. He calls persons to take up the cross and follow—to accept the life of self-sacrifice and suffering for the sake of the redemption and the salvation of many.

Wherever people respond to the will of God in Christ, there an aspect of the kingdom of God becomes visible to the world. The kingdom is present in the church even though church and kingdom are not identical. The reign of God is dynamic; it acts upon the church and through the church, making the church its agent or organ.

Jesus Fulfills God's Promises to Israel	
Old Testament	**New Testament**
Creation	New Creation in Christ *(2 Cor. 5:17)*
Temptation and Disobedience First Adam—all die	Christ, second Adam— all receive life *(1 Cor. 15:22)*
Disobedience of Adam	Obedience of Christ *(Romans 5:15)*
Promise to Abraham	Fulfillment in Jesus *(Mark 1:1-13; Luke 1:1-17; Gal. 3:6)*
Saved from Bondage in Egypt	Christ Saves from Bondage to Sin *(Matt. 1:21; Rom. 8:2)*
Covenant with Abraham	New Covenant in Christ *(Matt. 26:27, 28; Eph. 2:11-14)*
Kingship and Kingdom of Israel	Christ is King of Kings *(Matt. 21:2-11; Rev. 19:16)*
Prophetic and Priestly Vision	Fulfilled in Jesus, the prophet of the Highest *(Luke 1:76-79)* and the High Priest *(Heb. 5:5-10)*
(refer back to earlier chapters for fuller description of these terms)	

Fulfilling the prophetic mission

Jesus fulfilled the mission of the Old Testament prophets. We noted earlier how the prophetic word was related to the priestly ministry and to the word of wisdom. Jesus also took the law for granted. He said: "Think not that I have come to abolish the law and the prophets; I have come not to abolish them but to fulfill them" (Matt. 5:17).

At the same time this word, this law, as traditionally interpreted by the scribes, did not say everything. It pointed in the right direction, but it did not say enough. When Jesus looked at this tradition of interpretation, he felt that some of it must be rejected and some of it must go deeper. He often disagreed with the scribes in the way they applied this word to life. Jesus followed in the tradition of the prophets as he sensitively interpreted and applied the word to specific situations.

Jesus criticized much, in both word and deed. He exposed the hypocrisy of the Pharisees (Matt. 23:13-36) and all attempts to appear pious before people (Matt. 6:7, 16). He gave a different place to women, allowing them to sit at the feet of the teacher along with the men (Luke 10:38-42). He disregarded the barrier between Jews and Samaritans (John 4:1-30) and ate with publicans and sinners (Mark 2:15-17). These acts were in the tradition of the prophet—critiquing the life and teaching of the people of that day.

Further Reflections

1. We need to understand Jesus' ministry in the light of the history of God's revelation to his people and as reflected in the Old Testament. The whole story of God's revelation is an invitation to accept Christ and to follow him in life. Each major theme in the Old Testament contributes to our understanding of the life and ministry of Jesus. Each theme is a specific invitation to faith.

2. The progressive understanding of God's revelation needs to be taken into account when we interpret Scripture. To understand what God wills for us, we do need to look at the beginning of a line of interpretation; but more significantly, we must also look at the end or the goal of that interpretation. For example, early in Israel's history, when revenge was the usual practice, God's revelation was that revenge should no longer be practiced. One should not take more than an eye for an eye (Exod. 21:23-25). This was a truthful word in that setting; it prohibited a person from taking more than life for life. Later, however, God showed mercy to David and life was not required for life (2 Sam. 12:7-13). At this point, the truthful word said that it was not necessary to take life for life. Jesus' life and teachings moved even further; his way was forgiveness and love for the enemy. Paul, looking at this whole line of Old Testament teaching and Jesus' claim that he fulfilled the law (both negative and positive), concluded appropriately "Love is the fulfilling of the law" (Rom. 13:10).

Thus, when we look at the end of a line of revelation or an understanding of revelation, we can see it in perspective. Viewing the life and teachings of Jesus in this way allows us to see them in a different frame of reference. We see new dimensions to Jesus' teachings that we would have not been aware of otherwise. And the events of revelation that preceded the coming of Christ look different when we see them from the point of fulfillment.

In our interpretation of Scripture, it is helpful to notice the direction of Jesus' interpretations and then to follow that direction as we seek for understanding. This approach allows the Spirit of God to be active in our interpretation and helps us avoid a very narrow or legalistic interpretation.

3. It is appropriate for us to view Jesus in relation to the tradition of Judaism. All of us stand in a tradition, both religiously and culturally. When we see how Jesus responded to his tradition, then we know something about how we must respond to ours. We notice at least three things: (1) Jesus acknowledged his tradition and made it his own. He did not come to overthrow the law but to fulfill it. He accepted the sacred tradition of Israel as binding. (2) Jesus acknowledged that this tradition (Scripture) had been interpreted in ways that were no longer true to the intentions of that tradition. Such interpretations had to be rejected as the "tradition of men" (Mark 7:8). (3) Certain aspects of the tradition had to be deepened. The direction was correct but it did not go far enough. Where the tradition spoke of not killing, Jesus spoke of not hating in your heart (Matt. 5:21-26); where it spoke of not committing adultery, Jesus spoke of not lusting after another person (Matt. 5:27-30); where tradition said love might extend to those who love in return, Jesus said love included even the enemy (Matt. 5:43-48).

These three aspects of looking at one's tradition need to be part of our evaluation of our heritage. We need to identify fully with our Anabaptist roots. This is our tradition of understanding; it is the tradition that shapes our lives. But we also need to view it critically, rejecting what we no longer see as being true to the Gospel, and deepening those areas where we have received greater light.

The same movement will be seen in other settings as

well. People who come to faith in Christ from a totally different religious background will discover (1) aspects of their faith which they can without reservation affirm; (2) aspects of their earlier faith and practice which must be rejected; and (3) some aspects that they will understand more fully and deeply through their new faith in Christ.

God Invites Us

We are invited to receive Jesus as Lord. He is the fulfillment of all those acts of God through which Israel had come to know God: he is Creator, Redeemer, covenant Lord and King. The totality of God's invitation to faith comes to us in Jesus Christ, "For no other foundation can anyone lay than that which is laid, which is Jesus Christ" (1 Cor. 3:11), and "there is no other name under heaven given among men by which we must be saved" (Acts 4:12). Jesus is our invitation to faith.

9.
God Confirms
the Revelation

The themes that we have been studying—God's acts of creating, judging, promising, covenanting, saving, reigning—are central to the Christian faith. And in the last chapter, "Jesus Is Lord," we saw how Jesus is the fulfillment of these Old Testament themes. In light of this, we find it difficult to understand why Jesus was crucified. We wonder why Jesus wasn't welcomed with open arms. But a little reflection shows that it is not that simple.

The Promise of a Messiah
The scribes knew that Scripture needed interpretation; they saw their life-long task being to interpret the Scriptures. Yet only those interpretations which all the scribes or rabbis agreed to were considered binding. The scribes had given careful and detailed work to the passages which related to the coming Messiah. They recognized that many of the promises made in the Psalms with respect to the king had not yet been fulfilled, either in David or in any other king. These Psalms (such as Psa. 22 and 69) were recognized as messianic Psalms, which would be fulfilled at his coming. This was also true of many of the promises in the prophetic literature. Thus a body of material, which spoke of future events and of the Messiah, was sorted out; but it was difficult to relate these passages to each other.

A careful study of such passages points to at least two messiahs. Some of the prophecies clearly related to priestly functions—functions that belonged to the tribe of Levi. These, the scribes thought, would be fulfilled by a righteous teacher, coming in the lineage of Aaron and Levi. Other promises about establishing an everlasting kingdom were clearly made to King David and could only be fulfilled by a descendant of David. In the Qumran community, near the Dead Sea, these two messiahs were expected—the teacher of righteousness and the messiah or king. And as this was a priestly community, the first messiah received major emphasis.

In Israel's life the functions of the priest and the functions of the king belonged to two different tribes; on this basis, the prophecy seemed to point to the coming of two servants of God who would be instrumental in establishing the reign of God on earth. But other elements entered the picture as well, making it even more complicated.

The apostles, after the resurrection, referred repeatedly to Jesus' fulfillment of the suffering servant passages which begin in Isaiah 53. Yet in Judaism these passages were understood to be referring to Israel, not to the Messiah. Israel had suffered doubly for all her sins while in captivity in Babylon (Isa. 40:2). Through her suffering Israel had been cleansed from sin and prepared as a fit servant of God. Because of this suffering, Israel understood that God is Lord over all people and felt called to witness to this fact to all the nations. Through their suffering the people of Israel believed that many would come to believe in God. Thus Israel was seen as the one who had suffered vicariously for others.

This helps us understand why even the disciples at first had difficulty in seeing the suffering of Christ as a part of his messianic calling. When Jesus announced his suffering immediately after Peter had confessed that Jesus was the Messiah, Peter rebuked him; Peter could not imagine how the king, the Messiah, would have to suffer (Mark 8:31-32).

The problem of Jesus being both priest and king was not spoken to until the book of Hebrews was written. There the author says that Jesus serves in the heavenly tabernacle, not in the earthly one (Heb. 7; 9:24), and this affirms his priestly function. His Davidic line was of course confirmed in his birth.

Jesus Is the Christ

How then did the knowledge break through that Jesus was indeed the Christ? Mark's gospel helps to answer this question. Mark is writing to Greek Christians about Jesus. He wants to show how the disciples and those who followed Jesus came to know him as the Christ.

At the end of the first section of Mark (Mark 1:16—8:30), the confession that Jesus is the Messiah is made. The introduction to this section (Mark 1:1-13), however, is of a different nature; here Mark is saying that it is God himself who has confirmed Jesus to be the Christ.

"This is the beginning of the Gospel of Jesus Christ" (Mark 1:1). This caption speaks volumes if one knows the promises of the Old Testament. It says in effect that the gospel is, and that the man Jesus is the Christ, the anointed of God. Some manuscripts add "the son of God," probably because to the Jewish reader the Messiah was not necessarily understood to be a divine figure.

Mark begins by calling attention to the fulfillment of prophecy. He refers to Isaiah 40:3 and Malachi 3:1. The significant Old Testament reference, however, is Exodus 23:20, where Moses speaks of God sending an "angel" to bring the Israelites to the place he has prepared for them. But the word used for "angel" is the same as that used for "messenger" in the Isaiah and Malachi texts. Thus Isaiah 40:3 and Malachi 3:1 really interpret further the promise made through Moses. Mark is saying, in effect, that these promises have now been fulfilled. It is God's doing.

John the Baptist has come to prepare the way (Mark 1:4-8). He is not like other prophets, because he is the watershed between the old and the new covenants. At that time, Gentiles who accepted Judaism were baptized, indicating that they had broken with their former beliefs and life and had accepted the new life of service to God. John the Baptist, however, asks even Jews to repent and be baptized! This heralded the new life that was coming, even for Israel. In this way John was preparing the way for Jesus.

The Jews also expected that Elijah would return at the

end of days (Mal. 4:5); Mark shows that John the Baptist is in the image and tradition of Elijah—in his wilderness experience, in what he ate and wore, all the way to the belt which identifies him as a man of God after the image of Elijah (1 Sam. 1:8).

The main evidence that God himself has shown Jesus to be the Christ comes during Jesus' baptism (Mark 1:9-11). In his baptism Jesus identified with sinful humanity and fulfilled the requirement of the mediator—that of being one with the people (Heb. 5:1). Three items point to God's action of confirmation:

First, the heavens were opened. Isaiah had prayed: "O that thou wouldst rend the heavens and come down, that the mountains might quake at thy presence . . . to make thy name known to thy adversaries" (Isa. 64:1-2). Here now was the fulfillment. Not only were the heavens opened, but God's presence was with them in Jesus.

Second, the Holy Spirit descended on Jesus like a dove. This indicated that God was present in Christ, that God was incarnate in Jesus. The Holy Spirit in the form of a dove was a visible sign of God's presence.

Third, there was a voice from heaven. To the Jews this *Bath Qol* (literally, daughter of a voice, or echo) represented a specially significant word of God—a word to be noted as doubly binding. Here the voice of God is heard quoting a part of Psalm 2, a psalm used in the coronation of a king. The understanding was that the king became in a significant way the son of God at his coronation. Therefore the text reads, "You are my son, today I have begotten you" (Psa. 2:7). The last part of the verse is appropriately omitted in reference to Jesus, and the words "in thee I am well pleased" are added. This indicates that at this point Jesus entered his earthly ministry, a ministry of revealing himself to the world.

Significant here is the fact that God, through his own acts, shows in a threefold way that Jesus is indeed the Christ. God confirms that Jesus is the fulfillment of the promises.

Mark 1:12-13 indicates that Jesus was tempted and tested; through this Jesus showed himself to be a leader who would bring about the new era when there would be peace even with the animal kingdom (Isa. 11:6-9).

Thus in Mark 1:1-13, Mark has stated in essence that God himself has shown Jesus to be Christ, the Messiah.

Is He the Christ?

In the rest of his gospel Mark portrays how Jesus manifested himself to the people and how they struggled to know who he was and how he related to the revelation received earlier by Israel.

Jesus manifested himself in many ways, and this always brought the question, "Who is he? Could he be the one we are waiting for?" We will look at some of these instances in Mark's gospel.

1. Jesus had the power to call people into service for God. He called the four disciples and they left their father's nets to follow. In that day men, even though married, could not leave father and mother unless they invoked the law of Corban. This law allowed men to say that what they could earn for the family in their lifetime, they had given to God; then the parents had to let them go. It seems that the disciples recognized Jesus' right to issue such a divine call (Luke 5:1). The disciples followed, testifying that Jesus had the power to call them into God's service.

2. Jesus had authority in himself. He spoke with authority and yet not like the scribes (Mark 1:21-22). The scribes used only a mediated authority. They spoke in the name of Moses, and according to them even Moses did not speak in his own name but in the name of God. Thus, only God had the authority to speak, in his own name, a word of truth. But Jesus spoke in his own name. In the Sermon on the Mount he repeatedly contrasted the word of the rabbis with his own interpretation, saying "But I say unto you." This raised the question as to whether Jesus was God or perhaps an imposter.

3. In the temple Jesus cast out an unclean spirit (Mark 1:23-28). The significance of this event is clear to the witnesses. They ask, "What is this? A new teaching! With authority he commands even the unclean spirits, and they obey him." Can it be that Jesus has the power of God?

4. To the paralytic Jesus said, "Your sins are forgiven" (Mark 2:1-12). But the Jews knew that God alone could

forgive sins. Who then is this man who claims to forgive sins? Jesus knew they needed some visible evidence of his power in order to believe his word of forgiveness; so he heals the man of his paralysis. The people respond: "We have never seen it in this fashion." Could he in truth be God?

5. Jesus stilled the storm (Mark 4:35-41). But to send the storm and to still it is God's work. How can this man be doing the work of God? Who is he?

6. Only God has the power of life and death. But in a sequence of events (Mark 4:35—5:43) Mark shows Jesus saving people from death and even overcoming death itself. Jesus saves those who are in danger of their lives on the sea; he heals the Gerasene demoniac who is seeking his own death; he heals the woman who has been hemorrhaging for 12 years; and he restores Jairus' daughter to life. Who is this man who has the power of life and death? Powers that only God is said to have?

7. And in addition, Jesus was truly a shepherd, feeding his people as Moses fed the people in the wilderness (Mark 6:30-44) and leading them through deep waters as did Moses (Mark 6:45-52). Jesus fulfilled the promises related to the Messiah's coming, as he healed the deaf-mute (Mark 7:31-37), for Isaiah had spoken of such a time (Isa. 55:5).

No wonder that to those who were open to respond to him in faith and trust he was seen as the Messiah. No wonder that Peter could make the confession, "You are the Christ!" (Mark 8:27-30).

But some read the signs in a different way. The same events from Jesus' life and work are open to other interpretations:

1. The scribes did not believe that any human could forgive sins. They took Jesus to be as any other mortal and saw Jesus' claim to be presumptuous at best (Mark 2:1-7).

2. Jesus did not keep the Sabbath. He allowed his disciples to pluck ears of grain on the Sabbath. To the scribes this was a clear violation of the law. He healed a man's withered hand on the Sabbath. This could have waited until the next day and so clearly represented a violation of the Sabbath. Since it was also a deliberate act it

And the Word became flesh
and dwelt among us...

"You are the Christ
the Son of the living God."

God has made him
both Lord and Christ,
this Jesus whom you crucified.

meant he chose willfully to disobey God and so was worthy of death (Mark 3:1-6).

3. True, he cast out demons. But the scribes from Jerusalem argued that he did so by the power of Beelzebul (Mark 3:20-30). To show power is not enough. The real question is, who supplies the power—God or Satan?

4. Jesus did not abide by the traditions of the fathers or the rabbis. He did not fast as the scribes did (Mark 2:18-22); he ate with sinners which the scribes would not do (Mark 2:15-17). He did not show the qualities of a teacher in Israel. Jesus did not even keep the most elementary laws of washing hands before a meal! So, the scribes argued, he did not live according to the tradition handed down by the fathers (Mark 7:1-8).

Thus, rather than Jesus' revelation leading the scribes to faith, it led them to seek ways of bringing about his death. This is seen clearly in Mark 8:11-12. The scribes ask Jesus to give them a sign. (In John, a sign refers to a miracle; but in Mark it refers to the foretelling of an event.) At first they seem to be saying that if Jesus gives a sign and it comes true, they will believe him. But this is not their intent, for they already believe that he is a false teacher.

What the scribes wanted was for Jesus to give a sign; then when it was fulfilled they would use Deuteronomy 13:1-11 to condemn him. This is a reference to false prophets who will come and lead the people to serve false gods. The scribes' intent here was to make clear that Jesus was leading the people astray and needed to be judged. And so they took steps to crucify him.

The Confirmation of God

Mark's gospel shows two opposing interpretations of Jesus' public ministry. The disciples take him to be the Christ, the Messiah of God. They see him as fulfilling the promises of God and as doing the work of God. He could not be other than a prophet, the Elijah of God, who has come to vindicate the righteous sufferers. Jesus is, in truth, the Messiah. The disciples believe this to the extent that they are willing to follow him, and even to die with him.

The other interpretation of Jesus' ministry is given by the scribes and the chief priests. They hold Jesus to be a

God Promises

God Is Saving

Jesus Is Lord

God Confirms the Revelation

God Is Reigning

Responding to God

God Is Speaking

God Covenants With His People

God Is Creating

false teacher and a blasphemer. He does not show himself to be in the tradition of the rabbis, nor does he keep the law himself. How then can he be more than a blind leader of the blind? He is deserving of death. The scribes and chief priests believe this strongly enough to seek ways to put him to death.

Thus, this situation clearly had two contradictory interpretations. This often happened with the message of the prophets. Two sets of prophets claimed to speak for God, yet gave opposing interpretations. In such cases the people waited to see which word God would acknowledge, which word would actually come to pass. They waited for God's confirmation in history.

Jesus was crucified and the disciples felt that they must have been mistaken about Jesus. He did not become king; he was crucified. Their comment on the road to Damascus was, "We *had* hoped that he was the one to redeem Israel" (Luke 24:21). And the chief priests believed that, since Jesus did not come down from the cross to save himself, he was not vindicated in his claims and deserved to die.

God, however, acted to confirm the message of Jesus and the faith of the disciples. In raising Jesus from the dead, God confirmed Jesus' message and established his claim as being the truth. The disciples now became assured of their message: "Let all the house of Israel therefore know assuredly that God has made him both Lord and Christ, this Jesus whom you crucified" (Acts 2:36). No more evidence was needed, for in the resurrection God himself had spoken!

Further Confirmation

The final evidence will not be in until the end. God is not yet finished with the world and with his people. God is still active in creating, covenanting, saving, and establishing his kingdom, his reign on earth.

Each revelation of God anticipates a future. His creation has a beginning and moves toward an end of his own choosing. The beginning anticipates the end.

The promises of God point to future fulfillment. The promises of God made through the prophets have not yet been totally fulfilled; they await the time when God's will

will be done on earth as it is in heaven. Hebrews 11—12 shows clearly how the saints of God died looking forward to the fulfilling of God's promises to his people; and some have not even yet been fulfilled.

The salvation of God is experienced here and now in Christ. Through the new birth we have become new creatures in Christ. And yet, at the same time, there is a future aspect to salvation. We have not only been saved, but we will be saved and will receive the crown of life if we remain faithful to the end (Rev. 2:10).

The new covenant also awaits completion and consummation. In establishing this covenant at the Last Supper, Jesus refers to a future celebration: ''I shall not drink again of this fruit of the vine until that day when I drink it new with you in my Father's kingdom'' (Matt. 26:29).

In every way, God's revelation to Israel and God's revelation in Christ look forward to the time when Jesus Christ will be Lord of lords and King of kings (Rev. 19:16); when Christ will reign and his will be done, and all nations will come and worship him (Rev. 15:4). When God's judgments draw to a close, then the righteousness of God will be confirmed in the establishing of a new heaven and a new earth (Rev. 21:1-4). In this sense we wait for the final confirmation to come from God in a time of his own choosing.

God Invites Us

Each revelation is an invitation to faith. Each reveals God to us in a slightly different way. But in each revelation we are called and invited to respond in faith and trust to Jesus, who is the pioneer and perfector of our faith.

Bob Taylor

10.
Pilgrimage Through Early Adulthood

We have considered in our study thus far God's revelation—the revelation to Israel, to the early Christians, to us. We have noted how the people, at various times, understood the revelation of God and how they responded to that revelation. In these next four chapters, we approach our "invitation to faith" from a slightly different perspective: How do the life-stages of an adult Christian, the developmental tasks of our adult lives, relate to God's revelation and to our response to that revelation?

A Pilgrimage of Responsible Living
Life is a pilgrimage, a continuing process of living and learning. We are never at the same place twice; every event and every experience becomes a part of our further development and maturation. What we learn in one period of life lives on in the next; what we choose to do shapes the time to come. What we do not learn or fail to master at a given time restricts the future possibilities available to us. Thus we can speak in terms of a "pilgrimage of responsible living."

Educators speak of this pilgrimage in terms of developmental tasks. There are tasks that we must learn or master at given times in our growth from childhood to old age before we can move to a new level of maturity. Thus we must learn to walk before we can learn to run. Not to learn a given step when the teachable moment arrives is to restrict the possibilities of choices in that area of life.

"A developmental task is a task which arises at or about a certain period in the life of the individual, successful achievement of which leads to happiness and to success with later tasks, while failure leads to unhappiness in the individual, disapproval of society, and difficulty with later tasks." (R. J. Havighurst, *Human Development and Education,* McKay, 1953, p. 2). This indicates that humans do not respond to their environment in the same way as animals. Animals respond instinctively and immediately to the stimuli of the environment. But for humans, there is a broad range of possibilities for the development of body, mind, and spirit. What happens in a person's development is not a given from the beginning. It depends on many variables—variables of inner and outer forces and of personal values and choices.

People are created free moral agents. They are able to respond to God, to other people, and to the world about them in terms of goals and purposes freely chosen. In this sense people are open to the future. They can deliberate about what they should do, and they are free to choose that one action out of many which is most in harmony with their chosen goals.

The choices people make are real; they determine future history; they shape the rest of life's pilgrimage. Such choices have significance for the patterning of human life and for creating the structures of society in which all must live.

Developmental tasks are set for us by inner and outer forces and by values freely chosen in life. The *inner forces* have to do with the maturation of the body. New tasks are set for us by natural body growth, such as menstruation, which makes new physical and psychological possibilities available to us. Throughout life we face these physical changes to which we must adjust. Each age also brings about new psychological forces: marriage, the birth of a child, sickness, death, a change in jobs—and each time new psychological forces are set in motion.

Outer forces have to do with the demands of the

culture. The culture puts pressure on all of us to be socialized in much the same way as the rest of society. The home, the school, and the larger public are all agents of this continuing process of socialization. Not to respond appropriately to such forces leads to the disapproval of society.

Our freely chosen *values* also help determine how we will respond to various developmental tasks. Such values have become our own in a long process through childhood and adolescence. The values and norms given to us in childhood have been reassessed in adolescence. These early values have either been rejected and a new set of values chosen, or they have been accepted as our own freely chosen values. Thus, in early adulthood we act on values for which we are personally responsible. These represent our ethical and spiritual resources, our world view, our faith commitments.

But learning is not always constant. It is not evenly distributed over life's pilgrimage. Sometimes we learn at great speed. It is almost as if we re-work everything at one time, as if we reorient all of life around a new principle or value. Everything becomes new. Conversion is one example of this, but it also happens at other times. This can mean a complete reorienting of life.

At other times learning is on a plateau and we are hardly conscious of it. These are times of stabilization, of deepening the learning that has taken place earlier, of making that learning a fixed or permanent part of our lives. These plateau times are not problematic unless they halt or impede further learning.

There are also times of actual regression in learning, times when we are too frightened to assume new roles or responsibilities. When this happens we can not respond to the new tasks of development; instead we return to an earlier task and a known response for security and comfort. Growth is then impeded until this reluctance is removed or overcome.

Developmental Tasks of Early Adulthood

There are developmental tasks which all adults face during early adulthood. Some of the key tasks are the following:

*Today well - lived ...
makes every tomorrow
a vision of Hope*

—Anonymous

1. Deciding whether to be single or to be married. All young adults need to work through their values, aspirations, and life goals as they consider living as a single adult or seeking a marriage partner.

2. Developing new patterns of interrelatedness. Young adulthood is a time of forming deeper patterns for relating to other persons. The needs for warmth, affection, companionship, acceptance must be fulfilled through relationships with a marriage partner and/or close and intimate friends.

3. Deciding whether or not to have children. Young adults face the decision of starting a family—the possibility of giving birth to a child, of adopting a child, or of not having children. And if a child becomes part of the family, an additional task is that of parenthood.

4. Making a home. All young adults make decisions about where and how "home" will be—both the size and shape of the physical dwelling, the community or neighborhood in which it's located, and whether home is a single family or an extended family unit.

5. Preparing for and beginning vocations. Questions such as, "How will I earn a living?" and "What occupation(s) do I choose?" face all young adults. And once

the initial decision is made, the continuing task is moving into the vocation in healthy and happy ways.

6. Accepting civic responsibility. In early adulthood people are often preoccupied with their immediate tasks which focus in on themselves. But they also need to relate to the larger community; they need to be aware of and become involved in responsibilities related to church and community.

7. Developing a congenial social group. Young adults need to form a new group of friends or at least rework some old friendships. A nurturing and challenging group of friends which allows for the sharing of experiences—failures, successes, and hopes—is important at this time of life.

Response to These Tasks

How do young adults respond to the developmental tasks faced in early adulthood? We have considered how God's revelation came to Israel. We noticed the growth in their understanding of God and of their responsibility in life. How do these same basic principles apply to our developmental tasks?

1. We can approach each developmental task in terms of promise and fulfillment. God's promise to Abraham touched on those things he was immediately concerned with—a son, food, a meaningful future. The promise of God related directly to those immediate concerns of living.

God comes to us also through promise. In each developmental task we can find a promise. We wrestle with each task until out of it comes God's promise that, if we respond in a specific way, it will bring blessing to us and to others. Thus, wrestling with being childless may lead to the promise of children through adoption. Similarly in relating to a spouse or a friend, it is only as we hold out new promises to each other that a meaningful future for the relationship can be hoped for.

2. We can also approach our developmental tasks in terms of salvation. The message of the Exodus was one of liberation from bondage. In salvation through Christ the principalities and the powers of the world have been overcome. This says that as we meet developmental tasks, we

need not be bound by the expectations of culture or the structure of society. We are free to look at various options from the vantage point of the Christian faith and Christian values.

In our response to the various developmental tasks, we are not forced to make certain commitments. We are really free, free to marry or not marry, free to have children or not have children, free to take on specific civil responsibilities or decide to bypass civic involvement. This freedom gives us room to determine a positive direction of our own choosing.

There is the temptation to respond to developmental tasks by simply following the culturally expected norms, as though our response has already been determined for us. We need to experience liberation from such bondage, so that we can freely respond to the tasks before us. God comes in Christ to liberate us from bondage and frees us to be responsive to God as we face these tasks of life.

3. We can approach the developmental tasks as participants in God's creative work, for we are co-creators with God. Every task presents a new and important creative moment, a moment in which our response will help to shape the future. Thus, each developmental task needs to be welcomed, not as a task that represents a chore or a compulsion, but as a new opportunity and a challenge.

As co-creators with God we must name the world about us, we must observe and analyze the situations in which we find ourselves, so we can know what response to make. Knowing that our response shapes the future will cause us to pay closer attention to the ultimate values of faith which we wish to preserve.

We are asked to have dominion over the created order. The meeting of developmental tasks is one way in which we exercise this responsibility. If there is chaos in any area we need to bring to it a new structure, we need to order it so it moves toward life.

4. In the meeting of our developmental tasks we also meet with failure. Just as out of the human situation of freedom came fear and rebellion, so in our freedom we may respond in ways that lead to disorder and death rather than to life. Thus, in learning to relate to a spouse we may

seek to dominate and subdue rather than seek to become joint heirs of the grace of life. Subjugation of this kind is related to sin, not to obedience (Gen. 3:16).

Any of the developmental tasks can be approached in a sinful way. We can choose to marry for the wrong reasons, with false motives. We can seek luxury and wealth in a vocational choice, rather than personal happiness and service for others. Each task can be a step of disobedience and a means of self-exaltation—a grasping after making life autonomous. The more we respond selfishly to each task the more we distance ourselves from God, from each other, and from God's purposes for our lives.

Yes, we have to reckon with failure. At some point or other, false responses will be made that have to be overcome. Here we need to know that in spite of our sin, God is active through his grace to redeem and to restore. We need to be ready to acknowledge our failures to each other and to God; we need to repent and to seek forgiveness. When we turn to God in obedience, when we take a new direction toward life, then possibilities for healing and reconciliation and restoration are opened, then God's grace can operate.

5. Responding to developmental tasks is a form of covenanting. We covenant with God and with all persons who are involved with us in the facing of a specific task. As we move through the stages and tasks of life, we continue to form covenants.

For example, marriage is a covenant not only with one's spouse but also with God and all the people who are expected to honor that covenant. Only if one disregards the whole range of covenants with parents, friends, and loved ones, can one argue that what two people do between themselves is of no concern to others.

Whether as married persons or single persons, we are involved in a whole series of covenants. We are free as persons only as we find ourselves in fidelity to others and as we seek God's grace to do so. Every developmental task presents to us new covenantal relationships, which are gateways to fuller life.

6. The reign of God theme is also relevant to developmental tasks. We will meet each task on the basis of the

values and life objectives which we hold at that particular time. If we bring the values of the coming reign of God, then we will view the task from a specifically Christian orientation. We see the reign of God most clearly in the life and ministry of Jesus. So his life becomes a model for us, and we seek to bring his spirit and mind to each developmental task we face.

As we are clear about our ultimate values in life and as we make our day-to-day decisions based on those values, we will experience the Lordship of Christ in our lives. The reign of God, the will of God, thus becomes the criteria for choosing to meet our tasks in one way rather than another.

Just as in the time of Samuel when Israel chose to have a king, we too are aware that whatever choices we make, there will be some consequences to face. Once a direction is set, we are to remain loyal to the covenant we have made with God and with others. Thus if we choose marriage rather than singleness, what is required is faithfulness in that decision. If we choose singleness, we are to practice faithfulness to God and to others in that context. We are free to choose either one, but our life is to be lived under the reign of Christ in either choice.

7. The prophetic approach also has a contribution to make. Some things have been established over the years as normative. They are proclaimed to all; they have been termed the general will of God; they give the basic directions for life (such as the Ten Commandments). But these basic commands need to be translated into specific settings in the lives of specific persons. Here there needs to be a sensitive reading, a prophetic reading, of what is of God in the specific situation. Thus to buy a car may be ethically good in one setting but not in another; a response of love may take one form in a person who has an outgoing personality and take another form in a shy person.

More specifically, we need to prophetically examine the compromises we make with the world by living in its structures; are these compromises really of God, or do they represent disobedience more than obedience? Such critical evaluation of our culture is necessary for us as Christians, if we are to respond appropriately to the developmental tasks we face.

8. All of these ways of responding to the tasks of life are summed up in Christ. We are to face specific life tasks and to respond to particular situations out of lives that are lived under the Lordship of Christ.

We can respond with faith and trust and commitment to the promises of God that come to us through the developmental tasks in life. And as we do so, we will begin to experience the joyous signs of fulfillment which give hope for the future.

The Invitation

The developmental tasks of early adulthood represent an invitation to faith. They present specific settings, choices, and opportunities for the exercising of our faith; they present concrete realities of life to which we can respond in the context of faith. They present to us specific areas in which we can realize and experience the reign of God in our lives.

Bob Taylor

124

11.
Pilgrimage Through Middle Adulthood

Little formal attention has been paid to the pilgrimage of life beyond early adulthood. For the early adults there are books on living as a single person, books on courtship and marriage, guides to the nurture of children, and similar resources. These kinds of helps are few for persons in middle adulthood. Some books, such as Gail Sheehy's *Passages: The Predictable Crises of Adult Life,* point out the pitfalls of the middle years, but they are not very helpful in avoiding the pitfalls. Sometimes the impression is even given that unless a person has experienced all the pitfalls, he or she is not entirely normal or has not really lived.

The lack of positive help in this area may stem from the assumption that middle-aged adults are mature adults, who do not need to learn any more. Though we know this to be false, our operative principles are often based on this assumption. Universities are for young people; Sunday school is for children; adult education is often non-existent in the community or in church. These attitudes are changing, but only slowly.

This lack of informative help for middle adulthood may also result from our individualistic and success-oriented society. Each person is to make it on his or her own, on the job, in personal crisis, in managing family life. To do less, we seem to think, will somehow reflect negatively on us as persons.

The truth of the matter is that middle adults have as much to learn as anyone else. Middle adults face developmental tasks that are as significant as those faced earlier in life; in fact, the developmental tasks of the middle years may touch more people directly than was true in early adulthood. In these years things often go wrong in marriage relationships, in relationships with children, and in relation to one's job. During this time covenants are broken, families are neglected because of the demands of jobs and professions, and often the promise of the future is lost. If persons need help in any period of life, it is during middle adulthood. The tasks are formidable and the structures for helpfully dealing with the tasks are often missing.

Developmental Tasks of Middle Adulthood

The developmental tasks of middle adulthood include both the continuation of some of the young adult's tasks and the addition of several completely new tasks. Some of the key tasks which face middle-aged adults are the following:

1. Achieving civic and social responsibility. What has not been learned in this arena earlier must be caught up in the middle years. Our society calls mainly on middle-aged people to shoulder civic responsibilities and public services. Middle-aged adults are expected to make heavy commitments, in terms of finances and personal involvement, to many community concerns.

2. Establishing and maintaining an economic standard of living. Even though we might wish to deny this, we do have to acknowledge that our culture places this expectation upon adults. This is one criterion of success by which people are evaluated. Not only does the culture expect it, but growing family and educational goals also demand that careful attention be given to this area.

3. Assisting teenage children to become responsible and happy adults. This is a demanding and challenging task in a society that honors youth and technology at the expense of age and wisdom. It is not easy to help teenagers find the right amount of emotional security and dependence as over against the emotional independence needed. Another difficult area related to this task is that as children

become independent, adults may feel that they are no longer needed.

4. Relating to other significant persons. People in the middle years are so busy with jobs, financial obligations, and children that they tend to neglect or take for granted relationships to marriage partners or to other significant persons. But neglected relationships deteriorate. For example, once children need less attention, parents often wake up to the fact that they do not know each other as persons. Some persons have gone so far in their neglect that relationships are broken; other persons are able to renew their covenant with each other.

5. Developing adult leisure-time activities. Again many adults have been "too busy" to pay attention to the value of and the necessity for leisure activities. In choosing such activities, adults need to recognize the probability that the rugged sports of earlier years are no longer appropriate (not even the races of the Sunday school picnic). Leisure activities can be chosen with an eye to the future, determining things that can also be done in later life. Choosing such activities now allows time to master them sufficiently so that they will bring enjoyment in later life.

6. Accepting and adjusting to the many psychological changes of middle age. This takes into account the decline in physical capacity and the psychological adjustment which that requires. In a society in which the young and the beautiful are honored, there is often an unwillingness to accept graying hair, wrinkled skin, the letting out of the belt, and other changes which occur during middle adulthood. Many false responses, damaging to us and to the people we live with, are possible and are chosen all too often in an attempt to cover up signs of aging.

7. Adjusting to aging parents. Not only do adults in the middle years live with teenagers, they also often have to minister to aging parents at the same time. The nuclear family in our society often makes it difficult for grandchildren and grandparents to benefit from close contact with each other. And so the parents are caught in the middle. Thus many middle-aged adults are ministering to two sets of people, the young and the old, who are living in two separate worlds.

127

Growing Into Maturity

How then are middle-aged Christian adults called to respond to their developmental tasks? What relationship can we find between these tasks and the emphasis on growth and maturity in the Scriptures? Many of the biblical writers assume that Christians will grow in faith and knowledge; Jesus certainly stated that the law-and-order approach of the Pharisees was not the highest kind of maturity.

To look at these questions, we will turn to an in-depth study of a biblical text which speaks specifically about growth and maturity: Hebrews 5:11—6:3.

1. The writer of Hebrews 5:11—6:3 gives us a good lesson on Christian growth. He indicates that there is so much more that he has to say about Jesus, but the readers cannot hear it now; they have grown dull of hearing (Heb. 5:11). He means that his readers have not yet matured enough in their faith to grasp the significance of what he wants to say.

The writer also recognizes that the readers are not making the appropriate responses to the word, responses which would allow them to grow further in their knowledge of Christ. They ought to already be teachers (i.e., mature), but they are still in need of teaching on an elementary level; they have not matured enough to deal with these matters on a higher level of maturity (Heb. 5:12). Maturity clearly does not depend on how many years we have been Christian or on how many courses we have taken. It depends on the level of growth attained.

2. The writer infers that the readers need to be taught again the first principle of faith. This indicates that there has been an actual regression in growth. The writer clearly sees that one possibility in life is that people will regress; and when this happens then the elementary things must be re-learned. In terms of growth, there is no standing still. Either we will grow and mature or we will lose what we once had.

3. The writer also indicates in Hebrews 5:3 that the person who does not grow is unskilled in the Word of righteousness. Such a person cannot be trusted to distinguish between good and evil, cannot make sensitive distinctions

Growth has not only rewards and pleasures but also many intrinsic pains... Each step forward is a step into the unfamiliar... It means giving up something familiar and good and satisfying. It frequently means a parting and a separation. It often means giving up a simpler, easier and less effortful life, in exchange for a more demanding, more responsible, more difficult life. Growth requires courage, will, choice and strength.

—Abraham H. Maslow

between right and wrong. Even if such decisions are made, they will be made on a false base, on an elementary level, and not on the appropriate level of maturity. This is one of the major difficulties in responding to developmental tasks; it is often difficult to respond to these tasks with the level of maturity that is called for. Even as adults and as Christian adults, we are not always able to do so, and this causes difficulties for us and for others.

The problem here is one of growth or maturity. To be mature is to respond appropriately to the developmental tasks before us. When there is a lack of appropriate growth, the maturity needed for an appropriate response is also lacking.

When we do make an inappropriate response, we usually justify it by appealing to Scripture or some other accepted norm. But this must be seen as an attempt to cover our inadequacy, rather than as a sign of maturity or spirituality. The scribes had great difficulty in understanding Jesus at this point, but he would not allow them to hide behind an appeal to Scripture in this way.

Our frustrations with our response to the developmental tasks, especially where it leads to chaos rather than to life, may be a sign that we have not responded on the appropriate level of maturity. Becoming aware of this may help us to move on to a new level of maturity.

4. The writer of Hebrews has been leading up to a positive word. "Solid food is for the mature, for those who have their faculties trained by practice to distinguish good from evil" (Heb. 5:14). Difficult and complex problems do not need simplistic answers. They need mature responses and actions.

Maturity is not achieved except by practice, by being engaged in the issue all the time. Maturity is acquired through experience—through constant decision-making. Our decision-making abilities must be trained by practice, so that we can make sensitive distinctions and evaluations between what is good and what is evil.

Maturity does not come by book learning and college degrees alone; neither does it come only by being pious and zealous. Maturity comes by being Christian in the everyday practical decisions of life. Maturity comes as we apply our faith sensitively to the developmental tasks of life.

5. We are to leave the elementary doctrines and go on to maturity (Heb. 6:1-3). We have often taken the reverse to be true, saying that a return to the fundamental doctrines is a sign of maturity! The writer is not saying that fundamental doctrines are not foundational; they are. He is saying, rather, that we have to build on the foundation of elementary doctrines. That is, there are elementary levels of understanding the various doctrines, and there are mature levels of understanding the doctrines. The writer is encouraging the reader to attain a mature level in understanding the doctrines of faith and their relationship to life.

We probably have not reached a mature level of understanding until these doctrines are seen, not only as something to be believed, but rather as the way God has created the world. These basic doctrines are descriptive of life as it must be lived; they allow us to see the nature of our life under God and in the world. Each one of the doctrines we have so far considered describes part of the acts of God and the nature of our human response to what God has done.

Such discerning of Christian obligation, of our response to what God has done, needs to take place in the Christian community, in the church. The writer of Hebrews takes it for granted that we need daily to be exhorted (Heb. 3:13), that we must not neglect prayer (Heb. 4:14-16), nor the gathering together to admonish one another to love and to good work (Heb. 10:23-25). Thus, the church is the larger family from which we seek help, discernment, and strength, so we can act in accordance with the will of God. We need to make more of this binding and loosing function of the church as we meet and respond to the developmental tasks in our daily lives.

The Invitation

The developmental tasks of middle adulthood challenge us and invite us to respond with mature faith to the issues of life; as we do so, we will sow seeds of life rather than death, and receive the blessing of God in our lives.

Bob Taylor

12.
Pilgrimage Through Later Adulthood

Life's pilgrimage moves on—from young adulthood, through the middle years, and on into the later years. Later adulthood, the time when people, having moved through many full years of living, can offer to the community and the world the wisdom of experience. In the Old Testament records of Israelite history and life, we note the great appreciation for the wisdom of the aged (Job 12:12; Deut. 32:7; Exod. 20:12). And in various societies throughout history, older adults in the tribe or clan or community have been held in high esteem and contributed greatly to the life of their people.

Our own society, while at times giving lip service to the importance of its older members, often shows through attitudes and actions another way of viewing later adulthood. Many older adults are retired because a firm, a business organization, or the attitudes of society have retired them. They may not have chosen retirement, because there are still contributions they could make. But when society no longer expects anything of persons, when the operating principle is that older adults can no longer make a meaningful contribution, they are retired.

One area in which some older adults still feel they can make a contribution in this society is financially. They may appreciate this to the point that they give or leave everything to their children, even when the children do not really need and may not be good stewards of such gifts. Such action shows a hunger to be appreciated, a wanting to give to life, to contribute in meaningful ways.

The industrial society has called forth the nuclear family, in which mother and father and young children are a unit to themselves; this structure helps to alienate older adults from much of life. They are left to their own resources without adequate help for facing their developmental tasks. It is not that other people want to be hurtful; often they simply do not realize that older people also face formidable developmental tasks.

Perhaps younger and middle adults do not want to think ahead to the facing of these tasks of later adulthood themselves; thus they offer little help or understanding. The pretense is that the tasks of later adulthood are not there, that they do not constitute real challenges of faith, or that they really are not growth tasks at all. But all of this is to sell the tasks of later adulthood short, to fail to recognize the significance of the tasks of the later years.

The Developmental Tasks of Later Adulthood

The developmental tasks of the older adult cover many varied areas of growth. Some of the significant tasks are the following:

1. Adjusting to decreasing physical strength and health. This is a task even if persons have been spared sickness or accident. Many older people do have to adjust to sickness, invalidism, or some chronic illness; all face changes in physical energy. Such adjustments are not easy, especially if there is no one else to pick up the work that can no longer be done. Many older adults are forced to extend themselves beyond what is healthful simply because there are no other persons to rely on.

2. Adjusting to retirement and reduced income. This is a difficult task because in our culture retired persons are often seen as no longer being productive members of society. For persons whose lives have revolved around jobs, such a re-orientation for retirement can be quite difficult. This may also take away what meaning life has held.

When the worth of a person has been equated with success or productivity, then to cease producing means that one's worth has disappeared along with the job.

3. Adjusting to the death of a spouse. For many older persons this is a most significant learning task and can be a difficult adjustment. A couple reaching later years together have so learned to lean on each other that to lose the other is to lose much of one's own life. Very often a whole new set of relationships has to be sought, for couple-centered relationships are changed with the death of a spouse.

4. Establishing a healthy affiliation with one's age group. This needs to be accomplished without too complete a break from the life of one's children and grandchildren. The companionship with one's own age mates is extremely important, and often overt efforts must be made to ensure such contacts and fellowship.

5. Learning new ways of relating with one's children, who are now adults, and maintaining contact with the lives of grandchildren. In addition to contact with these members of the immediate family, the older adult also needs to continue relating to extended family units.

6. Meeting social and civic obligations. Older persons are often very capable and gifted in civic leadership. Many statesmen and church leaders have made their best contributions to the public in their older years. Certainly there are, among elderly persons, untapped resources for public service in church and society. But adults in their middle adult years often haven't seen this as a promise or a potentiality. And what they have not received as a promise, they cannot easily respond to in later adulthood. Thus this task often becomes difficult because proper groundwork has not been laid.

7. Establishing satisfactory physical living arrangements. Again the structures of the nuclear family and the structures of society often raise problems in meeting this task. Older persons may be forced to live by themselves until they must enter a nursing home. There are too few options in-between these extremes. Too many houses are poorly arranged for the aged and are not located near proper transportation. So much needs to be done; all too often so little is being done. Creative thought to living

arrangements for older adults needs to be given. And in the meantime, older adults need to master new methods of dealing with their physical living arrangements.

8. Preparing for the eventual end of life by building a set of beliefs that one can live with and die with in peace. The continuing growth of personal faith, the discovery of that which holds ultimate meaning in life, which in reality is a task at all ages, becomes a most significant developmental task in later adulthood.

Responding to These Tasks

In many cases, older adults need to be helped by others in order to meet their developmental tasks fully. But so often there have been few to help. Little wonder then that some older persons see their tasks as inviting death rather than as an invitation to life. Family, friends, and society can help to change this as they support older adults in their response to their tasks.

1. There is need for older adults and those working with them to strive for wholesome living, including both *shalem* (health) and *shalom* (peace); that is, health for body and spirit. This would require a wholistic approach that looks to the purposes of God for older adults.

In our society, however, we seem to have an illness-care system rather than a health-care system. That is, our emphasis is on curing illnesses rather than on healthful living. Society and often older adults themselves focus on solving the obvious problems of disease, inabilities, and living conditions, but pay little attention to healthful and wholesome living for older adults. The Christian community could offer much to our society by responding creatively to this need.

2. Attention needs to be given to overcoming structures that keep older adults in captivity or bondage. These structures are many and varied, and are found in many areas of life: proper housing, where the necessary degree of independence and dependence can be adjusted without leaving one's place of living; arrangements for meals so that a healthful diet is maintained—again adjusted to personal need; the financing and upkeep of large houses when persons are no longer physically able to work. There are

*When grace is joined
with wrinkles
it is adorable.
There is an unspeakable dawn
in happy old age.*

—Victor Hugo

many of these physical-structural problems needing attention.

More significant is the overcoming of structural problems that cause older adults to be isolated and to feel useless. We have already mentioned that the nuclear family pattern leaves older adults too much outside of the family. Retirement is also a problem if there seems to be no purpose in living, if nothing can take the place of accustomed work. Being retired from organizations and committees poses additional problems if nothing takes the place of such services in church and society.

Older adults who band together can use their considerable power and skill in business and organization to speak to some of these structural problems. If a promise of possibility and change can be experienced, then many things could happen.

One need is certainly pastoral care that counts; care that not only says "take heart," but also takes hold of some of the problems. This kind of pastoral care can be given by any concerned member of the church or society and also by the Christian community corporately.

In the Image of God

The response to the developmental tasks of later adulthood needs to take into account basic human needs. These basic human needs are best described in our opening chapter on creation. We noted earlier that all persons are created in the image of God. This has significant implications for older adults when we recognize what it means to be in the image of God.

1. First of all, being in the image of God means that we are personal beings created to relate and respond freely to God, to people, and to the world about us. Life loses its meaning when significant, free, and responsible personal relations cease. Thus older adults need to sustain meaningful inter-personal and inter-generational ties with others. These ties need to extend beyond the family, to be linked with all of society. Older adults need to continue finding promise for the future in relationships with others.

Older adults may need to be assisted by others in this task. In a time when older people were honored for their wisdom and counsel, they could meet this task on their own. Now where most significant responsibility has been shifted to middle age, if not to youth, older adults no longer have the power to accomplish this without willing cooperation from others. For example, if older adults know no young people intimately and by name, in whom they see hope for the future, they will have the feeling that all true values are being cast overboard. Learning to know some well-meaning, loving young people brings hope and a promise for the future.

2. Being in the image of God is also related to being co-creators with God. Older adults need to see themselves as continuing to be involved in God's task of ordering the world, in creating new possibilities for life. They may not need to build huge skyscrapers, but they do need creativity. They need to know that in older life they are bringing order out of chaos, naming the world about them so as to bring about life rather than death.

Again, in our society older adults cannot achieve this on their own if all responsibility for ordering life is taken into other hands. They need to be permitted to retain those opportunities and responsibilities they can still carry. When the creative edge to life is lost there is no promise and no hope.

3. A third aspect of being in the image of God is that people were given meaningful work to do. Work did not come as a result of sin. The charge to keep the garden was given before sin entered the picture. Sin affected the environment in which people would work, but work itself is simply part of what it means to be human. Work gives people the equilibrium to go on living. But older adults need more than work for work's sake; they need more than busy work. To be given busy work is to be demoted as a person. What is needed is work that has meaning to oneself, to others, and to God's reign on earth. What is needed is work that is human in the sense that it fulfills the command of God to his creatures.

Again, older adults cannot achieve this on their own, especially not in a society in which there is forced retirement and in which most things are assembly-line produced. Our society, and caring Christians in particular, needs to be creative in utilizing the resources of those who are retired and those who can no longer do hard physical labor.Though hobbies often help to fulfill the need for artistic expression, much more is needed. The contributions of older adults can be and need to be turned to the benefit of the whole of society.

4. To be in the image of God is also to be historically oriented, to be related to God's people past, present, and future. God has chosen to reveal himself to humankind in history. It is important therefore for all people to know themselves as part of this history.

In modern times with our emphasis on the new, we give the impression that history has nothing to teach us, that we have arrived and are self-sufficient in ourselves. This attitude effectively cuts off one of the most significant contributions older adults can make to society. They are the ones who can tell the stories of yesteryear; they are our immediate link with the past. My father-in-law, Hugo Bartel, broke the homestead sod with oxen and lived to watch Neil Armstrong step on the moon. What a span of history! What stories he can tell of many years! But is there anyone to listen?

All of us need to take time to listen to these accounts. If we listen, we will hear a part of our history; if we listen often and intently we will hear more and more significant aspects of that history. If we do not listen, but only talk, we will find that we hear only the same old stories from older adults— stories that begin with "When we were young . . . ," and then die away simply because there is no ear to hear.

Why not tape interviews with older adults? Be creative in asking them to respond to questions that cover a wide range of experiences and involvements. Church historical and archives committees could help with this project. It would make history come alive!

We are all part of a pilgrimage with God and his people. The pilgrimage does not stop with old age, only with death. And even then there is hope.

The Invitation

Later adulthood is an invitation to life. It is an invitation to cash in on a whole lifetime of experiences and observations about what is worthwhile in life; it is an invitation to help others center their lives around values and goals that have abiding significance.

Later adulthood is an invitation to faith—faith in the eternal purposes of God, in his love and mercy, in his power to bless beyond what we can ask or think. It is also an invitation to faith in God's people and the church—a faith that sees, in and behind the changes of the present, the hand of God. God's invitation to faith remains, as does his love.

Bob Taylor

142

13.
Whether I Live or Die

We can readily perceive two separate messages on death and dying: (1) the message of joyous hope in the resurrection as proclaimed by Paul (1 Cor. 15); and (2) the attempts of our modern culture to flee the thought of death and dying, yet at the same time being preoccupied with death.

Two Contrasting Messages

Paul lets us feel a ring of hope and anticipation as he speaks about the resurrection: "What is sown is perishable, what is raised is imperishable. It is sown in dishonor, it is raised in glory. It is sown in weakness, it is raised in power. It is sown a physical body, it is raised a spiritual body . . ." (1 Cor. 15:42-44).

Paul focuses, not on the morbidity of death, but rather on where death leads—to life. He speaks of our life with Adam being from dust to dust; but this means that our life with the second Adam, Christ, shall be from death to life. "Just as we have borne the image of the man of dust, we shall also bear the image of the man of heaven" (1 Cor. 15:49). Paul looks forward to the time when, in the twinkling of an eye, the dead shall be raised incorruptible. Small wonder that Paul could see death as serving life. "For to me to live is Christ, and to die is gain" (Phil. 1:21). In fact, Paul is ambivalent only about the time of his death. To continue living would mean further service to Christ and this is good; to die would be to be with Christ and that is far better (Phil. 1:23-26).

In this context death has lost its sting. There is no longer the fear of death; it does not hold life in bondage any more. It is not that death is eliminated; rather, death as the enemy has been overcome. The last enemy, death, has been overcome through hope born out of faith in Christ.

The contrasting picture of death is that portrayed in our culture. On the one hand we are preoccupied with death. It takes up front and center space in our newspapers and news reporting. If there are no reports of death, it has been an eventless day! Our TV sets thrive on death and the brush with death, though we don't want to see real people dying on the screen. The more death, the more successful the movie at the box office, especially if death and dying are portrayed in minute detail.

Upon closer examination, however, we notice that this is more an effort to escape death than to face the inevitability of death. It is precisely because deep down we know the inevitability of death that we seek to escape from it by this preoccupation with death. As we portray death apart from the normal human emotions that surround it, we are attempting to escape from facing death, we are avoiding its actuality for us.

When Paul looked at ultimate life, he looked past death to the new life in Christ. In our culture the true life is often seen as "The American Way of Life." It is the successful man, the youthful man, the beautiful woman, the self-made persons, the free people . . . and on and on. A premium is placed on the vigorous, confident, energetic, determined person. This is simply our culture's way of denying the reality of death.

Even on the personal level we have become death-denying. We do not see people die, for they die in hospitals or they just disappear from our homes. We do not talk to dying people or let them talk to us; we do not hear dying people speak because they are often drugged out of life— they simply fade away. Often we do not even want to see the dead person's body, for we like to remember them "as they lived." This saves us from grieving, for then we do not

144

O death,
 where is thy victory?

O death,
 where is thy sting?

Thanks be to God,
 who gives us the victory
 through our Lord Jesus Christ.

— 1 Corinthians 15 : 55, 57

remember the person to have died. When people die, we embalm them and put them in rust-defying caskets and in concrete vaults, as though to preserve the corpse forever.

The same death-denying fervor can be seen in the many ways in which we portray death as the enemy. Our whole illness-care system is pitted against death, even at the high cost of intensive care units. All our efforts are focused on seeking to live, and not on learning how to die.

Much could also be said about the absurdities surrounding our funeral rites and services. This has been well documented in Jessica Mitford's book, *The American Way of Death* (Simon & Schuster, 1963).

What is important here is to notice how in every way we seek to deny the reality of death. A good illustration of this is the fervent belief that our way of life, even our nation, must live forever. But no such thing is ordained of God. Only God's reign will live forever.

Preparing for Death

Until very recently we have not received much help in preparing for death. Not only have we been too busy with other things, but our whole culture has been against such an emphasis. Yet we do have some knowledge of former times when people were more ready to accept death as part of life.

In our time we have few occasions to witness death. We are kept away from the death-bed, and are not invited to share the dying moments of those who are close to us. Even when a couple is together until the moment when death separates them, they often talk about everything else rather than the impending death. Somehow, psychologically, we are not prepared to face death and we cannot talk about it—what would we say?

Sometimes the high level of technology set into operation near the point of death is not helpful in facing death. Extraordinary means of sustaining the body are possible —to the extent that the person is no longer conscious hours or days before death. When this happens, then death is hardly death. A legal, arbitrary definition for death must be sought, in order to know when to bury the corpse. This is certainly not helpful in teaching us how to die. Maybe it is just another way we have of not facing death nor allowing others to face death.

But we need to face death and we need to prepare for death. And the best way to prepare is to become more aware of how death is a part of life.

Dying Is a Part of Living

All of life is lived in the context of death. Any denying of this is seeking to live under an illusion. But this is hardly what is meant by dying being a part of life. Let's take a moment to look at our lives; what do we see? What is there which indicates that, for us, dying is a part of living?

1. Dying becomes a part of living when in all our living we reckon fully with our finiteness. This has many implications. It means living in such a way as to focus on values and ends that are of lasting worth; it means building relationships that count, rather than gaining possessions to leave behind. It means acting out of love, not greed; it means giving out of compassion, not out of compulsion; it means serving rather than ruling.

2. Dying is also part of living in another way. We experience death in our own lives while we are living. The most obvious way is through the death of people we love. We experience the pain of separation, together with joy, when people die in the Lord. We feel double pain for those who have not known Christ. Once we have experienced the nearness of death in the death of a loved one, we have to some degree come to know death ourselves.

We experience death also in other forms of loss. In the loss of health, in the loss of relationships, in the loss of limbs, in the loss of irreplaceable possessions or objects, we face a kind of dying. I still know the person I was before I had polio. I was active in sports and did many things I can no longer do. But I have had to lay that person I once was to rest. He has in a sense died and is no more. A process of grief is necessary in order to come to terms with the continuing of life after such a loss. The same experience is also present when friends fall out with each other or when marriage or other covenants are broken. We experience death in so many ways in our living that we should be able to talk about death to each other.

147

3. Dying is a part of our lives when we are separated from our community, when meaningful relationships do not exist. T. S. Eliot said, "What life have you, if you have not life together? There is no life that is not in community, and no community not lived in the presence of God." (Quoted in R. M. Herhold, *Learning to Die, Learning to Live,* Philadelphia: Fortress Press, 1976, p. 36).

The obvious case has already been mentioned—where the body functions are maintained long after all meaningful communication with loved ones has ceased. However, having been in such a non-communicative state several times, I can relate that I was aware of much more around me than even the doctors realized. But this does not deny that there is a point at which all communication ceases, never to be resumed. Death has then come to that person in this network of relationships.

Another form of death is what is often termed a "living death," being separated from all meaningful relationships to others. As one widow put it, "No one touches me any more." Her sense of lonesomeness and of being alone was frightening. It is even possible to be utterly alone in the midst of a crowd of people, even people we know.

Many people are existing in such a state of living death because they are without meaningful personal relationships. They cannot relate to life at any significant points. One person was happy that for once in many, many years she had been invited to a wedding. This was a great occasion in which she could participate in life. Most of her life lacked such participation. And often we are not even aware of people who are experiencing this living death.

4. Perhaps the most significant way in which we face death in the midst of life is in conversion. When we realize that our self-seeking life leads not to life, but to death, then we are ready to face death in order that we might have life. Paul speaks of dying with Christ and being buried with him (Col. 2:12). He says, "Put to death, therefore, what is earthly in you" (Col. 3) and then lists those things to which we must die in order to live.

This thought, however, could not be sustained apart from the thought of becoming alive in Christ through death. When Paul speaks of being buried with Christ, he also

What life have you,
if you have not life together ?
There is no life
that is not in community
and no community
not lived in the
presence of God.

— T. S. Eliot

speaks about being raised with him through faith in the working of God (Col. 2:12) and about putting on those things that make for life (Col. 3:12-17).

In this combination of death and resurrection Paul can speak of dying to the law, to self, and to works (Rom. 7:4; 2 Cor. 2:15-16; Eph. 2:8-9). It is in dying that we receive life as Jesus himself has said (John 12:24). If we are in Christ, therefore, we have died to sin and been raised to newness of life. In a sense we already stand on the other side of death and need not fear death any more. Death has lost its sting. We know about death because it is part of our experience, but it no longer holds us in bondage.

Dying, Our Opportunity

Even dying holds out a promise to us. It holds out the promise that, if we enter in upon it with trust and commitment, we will experience the presence and power of God in the pilgrimage toward death.

1. The time of dying promises to be a time of ordering our lives. I recall the expectations in our rural farm communities that if someone was on a deathbed, various persons would be called in and their life together reviewed. Where there had been hurts or betrayals, they would be made right through restitution or forgiveness. Sudden deaths were considered to be a problem because they did not give time to order life.

Where life has been secularized and offers no more promise in this life or the next, death is seen as the end of all things. Then people wish for a sudden death so they don't have to experience dying. For the Christian, however, dying has its promise.

2. Dying promises to be a time for the healing of relationships and a deepening of commitments of love. This healing can come through mutual forgiveness or through the receiving of peace at the hands of God. My father was not able to make things right with those whom he felt had wronged him. He sought repeatedly to have the matter resolved, first on a personal level, then with witnesses, and finally by taking it to the church (Matt. 18:15-17). The matter was still unresolved. Then, before his death, he took a match and burned his account of these painful years and all

the evidence related to the events, with the suggestion that the Lord will judge justly when he reviews the case (1 Pet. 2:23). He then had peace and this matter never preoccupied his mind again.

Loved ones who openly, honestly, and in the strength of God's grace have faced death together have known it to be a deepening of their commitment to each other and to God. It has made life worth living. This has been not only a time of reviewing life together, of sorting the wheat from the chaff, but also a time of experiencing the signs of fulfillment of the promise of death. They have already experienced together the new life that comes out of death. They have a foretaste of that which will yet be.

3. Dying holds out the promise of the fulfillment of hope. As humans we are open to the future; we act on the basis of hope. We act on the basis of "the assurance of things hoped for, the conviction of things not seen" (Heb. 11:1). We project the direction of history on the basis of God's history with humankind in the past. On the basis of what God has already revealed, we project the ends and purposes that God is working toward in history. Thus, as Christians, we are always informed by our hope, by our view of God's end in history. For example, on the basis of Christ's resurrection, we hope in the resurrection and can even now already walk and live in this hope.

Dying brings to us the promise of this hope, not only hope of the resurrection but of all of the promises of God that have become meaningful to us. Note the many items mentioned as objects of hope in Hebrews 11. Dying calls attention to death as a gateway to fulfillment, not as the end of all things. In dying we receive new hope.

4. Dying presents the promise of a last will and testament. So often in Scripture a final parting blessing is given by the dying person. This practice also came quite naturally when sick persons were cared for in their homes. Though the setting is different now, the need for a final communication with friends, loved ones, and the world, remains.

This communication can indeed be through a last will and testament as a legal and binding final stewardship of our property and possessions. We have more of a responsibility in this respect than we often assume. Probably, in most cases, it is not good stewardship to leave everything to the children. Causes and institutions that we have supported in life should be remembered in dying. Here again we can be co-creators with God in the ordering of life.

But we must also think about verbal, personal communication with loved ones and with friends. In dying, we can distinguish much more clearly between what was worth doing in life and what was simply a marking of time, or even worse a flailing of the wind. Where we receive this clarity of insight of what will be blessed or judged of God, we owe it to our loved ones to pass it on. This is not, however, the place for a "Get even" session with anybody. Let God do the judging.

Where there is a longer approach to death, or even from the time of our middle years on, we have the opportunity to record a personal history as a legacy to leave to others. This may be for the immediate family or for the larger community. It fulfills our obligation to evaluate the individual life in the context of the ongoing community. Out of this larger perspective, then, may come a very personal, focused charge to other persons about what they can contribute to this ongoing life of the community.

5. Some of us may be called upon to know the promise of suffering. Illness and suffering are not to be seen only as enemies in our lives. We need only to contemplate what it would be like if there were no release from this life. So illness and suffering may visit us, not only as enemies, but also with promise.

This is not to say we should invite sickness or not seek relief from pain. Rather it is to suggest that there is a promise for us also in suffering. Some of these promises may be seen in what suffering does for us in focusing our lives, in causing us to cease our endless business. Suffering also may cause us to appreciate health or to re-orient our lives in helpful ways.

We are also concerned, however, about that suffering for which we have no such positive rationalizations, the suffering that comes we know not why. Job wrestled with this kind of suffering. The purposes of his suffering were hidden to his rational reflection. He could understand neither the reasons for his suffering nor the justice of God in allowing

152

it. The purposes were hidden in God. What Job did learn was to rely on God, to trust in God in spite of his suffering. Job committed himself to the One who will judge justly and deal mercifully in a saving way with his children. Thus to the end of our pilgrimage also, it will be a pilgrimage of faith. The invitation to faith remains even in suffering and death.

In Conclusion

We have looked at living in the early, middle, and later adult years in earlier chapters. In this chapter we have focused on dying. We have taken one of the themes present in *Invited to Faith,* that of promise, and looked at some of the promises that dying presents to us. You may also want to take the themes of creation, fall, salvation, covenant, kingship, and the prophetic word, and apply them in the same way to dying. Each theme will bring a new perspective to our understanding of death and dying.

In the same way these themes give us a basic way to look at life. Individually and together, they present to us an invitation to faith. Each theme uplifts a way in which God is actively revealing himself to us; each theme also calls us to find the appropriate response of faith and obedience. And from God's revelation to us and our response in obedience, we will learn to know the truth that will make us free.

Epilogue

We have surveyed in these chapters the many ways in which God, through his revelation, has invited us to faith. God has revealed himself in diverse ways (Heb. 1:1) over a long period of time, calling forth faith and commitment from his people. Faith is not only believing that something is true; faith is also a total commitment of heart, soul, mind, and spirit to God.

Every person lives by faith. All people act out of a set of beliefs and values to which they are committed in faith. The issue then is living by one faith over against another faith; the question becomes *what kind of faith* do we have and *in whom* do we believe? In *Invited to Faith,* we have tried to show that our faith is manifest in our response to the acts of God, acts of revelation and salvation.

The response of faith to the Creator is one of adoration and praise. It is manifested in the worship of God and in the acceptance of the awe-inspiring responsibility of being co-creators with God.

When people do not respond in trust and commitment to God, this is manifested in their rebellion and sin toward God. The result is being separated and alienated from God.

The response of faith, however, recognizes God's graciousness to forgive sin and meets God's mercy with repentance and a plea for forgiveness.

Faith's response to God's promise is one of trust and commitment. Faith trusts in God's faithfulness, and commits the person to God's command with promise in the full expectation that God will keep the promise.

To God's deliverance from bondage (i.e. Egypt), faith responds with thanksgiving for salvation full and free. To God's binding covenant (i.e. Sinai), faith responds with the commitment to do all that God has commanded.

Faith recognizes that the Lord God is King; that God's will is to be done on earth as it is in heaven. The response of faith is one of obedience to the will of God, knowing that it will lead to the furtherance of the kingdom.

Whenever and wherever God sends his messengers (i.e. prophets) to speak specific words of warning or judgment, faith responds by hearing; such a hearing leads to repentance, to turning again to God, and to a new commitment to the will of God.

The revelation of God was most fully given in Jesus Christ incarnate. To this revelation of God's love on the cross, faith responds in all of the ways mentioned above. Faith is the response of praise and gratitude to the author and finisher of our faith (Heb. 12:2); it is a response of trust and commitment to him who has called us to follow; it is a response of thanksgiving for salvation and a dedication of one's life to his Lordship; it is a response of obedience to his will and a willingness to let his spirit speak of sin and of judgment and of righteousness in our lives (John 16:8-11). Jesus' summary is that whoever believes in him will not perish but have everlasting life (John 3:16).

When we look at our response to life on the basis of this faith, we ask how such faith in Christ ought to find manifestation in the way in which we respond to specific tasks and decisions in life. The developmental tasks we face vary from one time to another in our lives; yet in each period and in each task we need to express in and through that task our faith in Christ.

As a response to God's revelation to us, and in all areas of our life, *we are invited to faith.*

Bibliography

Bible Dictionaries

Blair, Edward P. *Abingdon Bible Handbook.* Nashville: Abingdon, 1975.

Buttrick, G. A.; and Crim, Keith R., eds. *The Interpreter's Dictionary of the Bible.* 5 volumes. Nashville: Abingdon, 1976.

Douglas, J. D., ed. *The New Bible Dictionary.* Grand Rapids: Eerdmans, 1962.

Miller, M. S. and J. L. *Harper's Bible Dictionary.* New York: Harpers, 1952.*

Richardson, Alan, ed. *A Theological Word Book of the Bible.* New York: Macmillan, 1962.

Tenney, M. C., ed. *The Zondervan Pictorial Encyclopedia of the Bible.* 5 volumes. Grand Rapids: Zondervan, 1975.

The Church Library should have one of the five-volume sets plus one or more of the one-volume dictionaries.

Old Testament (General)

Albright, William F. *The Biblical Period from Abraham to Ezra: A Historical Survey.* Scranton: Harper & Row, 1950.

Bright, John. *A History of Israel.* Philadelphia: Westminster, 1972.

Bruce, Frederick F., ed. *Israel and the Nations.* Grand Rapids: Eerdmans, 1963.

Westermann, Claus, ed. *Handbook to the Old Testament.* Minneapolis: Augsburg, 1967.

New Testament (General)

Hunter, Archibald M. *Introducing the New Testament.* Philadelphia: Westminster, 3rd ed., 1973.

Kümmel, W. G. *Introduction to the New Testament.* Nashville: Abingdon, 1975.

Lohse, Edward. *The New Testament Environment.* tr. by John E. Steely. Nashville: Abingdon, 1976.

Theology & Doctrine

Harder, Helmut. *Guide to Faith.* Newton: Faith and Life Press, 1979.

Neill, Stephen. *Jesus Through Many Eyes.* (Introduction to the Theology of the New Testament). Philadelphia: Fortress, 1976.

Schroeder, David. *Learning to Know the Bible.* Newton: Faith & Life Press, 1966.

Creation

Reumann, John. *Creation and New Creation.* Minneapolis: Augsburg, 1973.*

Westermann, Claus. *Creation.* tr. by John J. Scullion. Philadelphia: Fortress, 1974.

_____ *The Genesis Accounts of Creation.* Philadelphia: Fortress, 1964.

_____ *A Thousand Years and A Day: Our Time in the Old Testament.* Philadelphia: Fortress, 1962.

Covenant

McCarthy, Dennis. *Old Testament Covenant* (A Survey of Current Opinions). Atlanta: John Knox, 1972.

Mendenhall, George E. *Law and Covenant in Israel and the Ancient Near East.* Pittsburgh: Biblical Colloquium, 1955.*

Newman, Murray L. *The People of the Covenant: A study of Israel from Moses to the Monarchy.* Nashville: Abingdon, 1962.*

Kingdom

Bright, John. *The Kingdom of God.* Nashville: Abingdon, 1953.

Ladd, G. E. *Jesus and the Kingdom.* New York: Harpers, 1964.

Reuther, Rosemary R. *The Radical Kingdom.* New York: Harpers, 1970.*

Schroeder, David, et. al. *The Kingdom of God and the Way of Peace.* Mennonite World Conference, 528 East Madison St., Lombard, Il., 1979.

Wright, G. Ernest. *The Rule of God.* Garden City, New York: Doubleday, 1960.

Prophetic

Brueggemann, Walter. *The Prophetic Imagination.* Philadelphia: Fortress Press, 1978.

Clements, R. E. *Prophecy and Tradition.* Atlanta: John Knox, 1975.

Pilgrimage Through Life

Fowler, Jim; and Keen, Sam. *Life Maps: Conversations on the Journey of Faith.* Waco: Word Books, 1978.

Gleason, John J. Jr., *Growing up to God: Eight Steps in Religious Development.* Nashville: Abingdon, 1975.

Havighurst, Robert J. *Developmental Tasks and Education.* New York: David McKay, 1979.

Levinson, Daniel J., et. al. *The Seasons of a Man's Life.* Westminster: Knopf, 1978.

Sheehy, Gail. *Passages.* New York: Bantam, 1977.

Sherrill, Lewis Joseph. *The Struggle of the Soul.* New York: Macmillan, 1951, 1975.

Whitehead, Evelyn Eaton and James D. *Christian Life Patterns: The Psychological Challenges and Religious Invitations of Adult Life.* Garden City, New York: Doubleday, 1979.

Aging

Eshbach, Warren; and Kline, Harvey. *A Future with Hope.* Elgin: The Brethren Press, 1978.

Howe, Reuel L. *Live All Your Life.* Waco: Word Incorporated, 1976.

Nouwen, Henri J. M. & Gaffney, Walter J. *Aging: The Fulfillment of Life.* Garden City, New York: Doubleday, 1974.

Death

Bailey, Lloyd R., Sr. *Biblical Perspectives on Death.* eds. Walter Brueggemann & John R. Donahue. Philadelphia: Fortress, 1978.

Davidson, Glen W. *Living With Dying.* Minneapolis: Augsburg, 1975.

Grollman, Earl A. *Concerning Death: A Practical Guide for the Living.* Boston: Beacon, 1974.

Herhold, Robert M. *Learning to Die; Learning to Live.* Philadelphia: Fortress, 1976.

Mitford, Jessica, et. al. *The American Way of Death.* New York: Simon & Shuster, 1972.*

Shepard, Martin, M. D. *Someone You Love Is Dying.* New York: Charter Books, 1979.

*Indicates out of print, but available in some libraries.

STORY HOUR

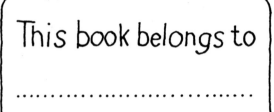

This book belongs to

....

Library of Congress Cataloging in Publication Data:
Hill, Eric. Good morning, Baby bear. SUMMARY: Baby Bear
wakes up, washes, has his breakfast, and is ready to begin his
day. [1. Bears—Fiction. 2. Morning—Fiction]
I.Title. PZ7.H5516Go 1984 [E] 83-43135 ISBN: 0-394-
86571-5 (trade); 0-394-96571-X (lib. bdg.)

Eric Hill

Good Morning, Baby Bear

Random House 🏠 **New York**

Wake up, Baby Bear.

It's a lovely morning!

A wash before breakfast.

What a clean Baby Bear!

Baby Bear is thirsty...

and hungry.

Breakfast is over.

Down we go!

Now it's playtime for Baby Bea

Have a nice day!